Leaving Certificate
Vocational Programme (LCVP)

Contents

Student Study Essentials

Online Study Hub – visit **www.edco.ie/onlinestudyhub**

Completed
(✓)

Leaving Certificate Vocational Programme (LCVP)
Guide to Better Grades

In addition to your other subjects, LCVP students follow two Link Modules for the Leaving Certificate:

- Link Module I – Preparation for the World of Work
- Link Module II – Enterprise Education

The two Link Modules are treated as one unit for assessment, which is at a **common level** (there is no Higher Level or Ordinary Level).

For the two years leading up to your Leaving Certificate, you will have been working on your Portfolio of Coursework. It will be assessed at the end of your final year. The portfolio represents 60% of your total marks for Link Modules.

Link Modules Written Examination

The Link Modules written examination takes place in May. It represents **40%** of the total marks for Link Modules.

You will have **two-and-a-half hours** for the examination, which is divided into **three sections**. You should become familiar with the **structure** of the written paper so that you will be well prepared for the exam.

		160 Marks	2.5 hours (150 minutes)
Section A	Audio Visual Presentation	30 marks	Allow 30 minutes
Section B	Case Study	30 marks	Allow 25 minutes
Section C	General Questions You must answer 4 questions out of 6	100 marks (4 x 25)	Allow 23 minutes for each question (4 x 23)

Section A: Audio Visual Presentation　(30 marks)

(Allow 30 minutes)

For Section A, you will be shown a **6-minute DVD** about a business or community enterprise.

There are usually **8 questions** in this section. There is **no choice** in this section. You must answer all the questions. Remember to allow more time for the last two questions as they carry more marks.

You will have **3 minutes** before the DVD begins. Use this time to **read the questions carefully**. Decide what the examiner is asking in each question. What information is required? Write down **key words** beside each question. Don't panic! Be ready to catch what is on the DVD and find the correct answers.

The DVD will be shown **3 times**.

The first time you see the DVD, watch and listen closely and **take notes** on the rough-work page about **what you see and hear**.

The second time, the DVD will be shown in **three parts**. Before each part is shown, you will be given **1 minute** to read the questions relating to that part. After each part is shown, you will have **2 minutes** to write your answers in the answer book.

The third time, you will see the full DVD again. **Check** that your answers are correct. **Explain** your answers, where necessary. **Watch out for anything that you might have missed**.

Remember to give **more detailed answers** for the **final two questions**. First, answer the question. Then **explain** your answer. Finally, think about connections with what you have experienced on the LCVP programme. Use **relevant examples** from your experience.

Section B: Case Study　(30 marks)

(Allow 25 minutes)

Before the exam

You will be given the Case Study **four weeks** before the exam. **Study** it carefully. **Analyse** it. Make sure that you are very familiar with it and understand all aspects of it.

Revise the **Specific Learning Outcomes** (SLOs) you have covered on the programme. How could they be applied to the Case Study? Think of questions that might be asked, and practise answering them. Think of how the Case Study relates to what you have learned and experienced on the LCVP programme.

On the day of the exam

There are usually **3 questions** in Section B. There is no choice in this section. You must answer **all** the questions.

First, **read the questions carefully**. What is the examiner asking? You must answer the question that is being asked — it may not be one that you had prepared for!

Some questions will have more than one part. Remember to answer **every part** of each question.

When answering the questions, remember to **explain** your answer. Where possible, use **relevant examples** from your experience.

Section C: General Questions   (100 marks)

(Allow 23 minutes per question = 92 minutes)

There are **six** questions in Section C. Each question is worth **25 marks**. You should answer **any four** questions.

First, **read** the **Index and Summary** on the first page of the section. This contains all the questions. It also tells you which pages they are on. **Choose** which **four** questions you will answer. **Decide** which question you will answer first. It's often a good idea to **answer the easiest question first**. Turn to the appropriate page in the exam booklet.

Do not spend more than **23 minutes** on each question.

Read each question carefully. What is the examiner asking? Each question contains a number of parts. You must **answer all parts** of each question you choose. Spend more time on the parts of the question that carry more marks.

When answering the questions, remember to **explain** your answer. Where possible, use **relevant examples** from your experience.

Even if you're unsure of the question, **always attempt an answer**. You will not get any marks for leaving a blank space, but you might get marks for an attempt!

Language used in the exam

Being familiar with the language used in Section C will help you when framing your answers. Below is a list of words often used in the general questions. Learn what the words mean, so that you will recognise them in the paper and understand what you need to do.

Word	Meaning
analyse	to study a problem in detail by breaking it down into various parts and examining possible relationships
apply	to bring knowledge or skills into use for a particular purpose
comment	to express an opinion about something
compare	to examine two or more things in order to discover their similarities or differences
contrast	to show the difference(s) between
criterion	a standard by which something can be judged or decided
characteristics	distinguishing qualities or attributes of an individual or object
define	to state the precise meaning of
describe	to give an account of a person, relationship, event, organisation or location
draft	to draw up a document, letter, report
evaluate	to find or determine the worth, value or significance of something; to assess or make a judgement
explain	to make clear in a detailed manner
identify	to show recognition of something
illustrate	to make clear by means of examples, charts, diagrams, etc.
indicate	to point out or state briefly

Word	Meaning
list	to write down a number of names or objects having something in common
mention	to refer to briefly
outline	to give a short summary of the important features of a subject
qualities	the distinguishing characteristics or attributes of an individual or object
suggest	to put forward an idea or plan

Preparing for the Exam

You will have been working on your **Portfolio of Coursework** for the two years leading up to your Leaving Certificate. Keep a copy of it and use it to help you to revise for the written exam. Read through it several times so that you are very familiar with its **layout** and **content**. Layout and content will be important when you are writing your exam answers.

Revise all of the **Specific Learning Outcomes** (SLOs). Be sure that you understand them and will be able to refer to them in your answers. They may be especially useful in answering the questions on the Case Study in Section B.

Learn the language of the exam. Use the list above to learn the list of words often used in the exam paper. **Revise** the words and test yourself on their meanings. It is very important that you understand the question fully and know how to answer it.

Learn what is meant by the **PEP** approach to learning — **P**re-Experience, **E**xperience and **P**ost-Experience. This is part of the learning cycle of LCVP. Use it when you structure your answers that relate to your LCVP experiences.

Remember: The examiner wants to give you marks. Always help the examiner by writing what you know about the topic.

Good luck!

Tick each question as you complete it and again once you have finished an entire exam paper.

LEAVING CERTIFICATE LCVP	TIME	2022	2021	2020	2019	2018	2017	2016	2015
Written Paper (160 marks)	**2 hrs 30 mins**								
Section A – Audio Visual (30 marks) *Answer all **8** questions	30 mins								
Question 1									
Question 2									
Question 3									
Question 4									
Question 5									
Question 6									
Question 7									
Question 8									
Section B – Case Study (30 marks) *Answer all **3** questions	25 mins								
Question 1									
Question 2									
Question 3									

(Continued)

Map Your Progress!

Map Your Progress!

LEAVING CERTIFICATE LCVP	TIME	2022	2021	2020	2019	2018	2017	2016	2015
Section C – General Questions **(100 marks – 25 marks each)** *Answer **4** out of 6 questions	23 mins per question								
Question 1									
Question 2									
Question 3									
Question 4									
Question 5									
Question 6									
Exam Complete									

Remember

- The written paper makes up 40% of the total marks for this subject. The Portfolio of Coursework accounts for the remaining 60% of the total mark.

- Write all answers in the written examination in your answer book.

- You must answer **all** questions in both Section A and Section B, and **four** out of six questions in Section C.

Study Hub

Your free online guide to smarter study.

Visit

www.edco.ie/onlinestudyhub

Leaving Cert Grades & CAO Points Chart

Higher % marks	Grade	Points		Ordinary % marks	Grade	Points
90–100	H1	100				
80 < 90	H2	88				
70 < 80	H3	77				
60 < 70	H4	66				
50 < 60	H5	56		90–100	O1	56
40 < 50	H6	46		80 < 90	O2	46
30 < 40	H7	37		70 < 80	O3	37
0 < 30	H8	0		60 < 70	O4	28
				50 < 60	O5	20
				40 < 50	O6	12
				30 < 40	O7	0
				0 < 30	O8	0

With the introduction in 2017 of the new Leaving Certificate grades, point will be awarded for LCVP Link Modules of follows:

LCVP link modules grade	current points	revised points
Distinction	70	66
Merit	50	46
Pass	30	28

Source: CAO

2022L462C1EL

2022

Coimisiún na Scrúduithe Stáit
State Examinations Commission

Leaving Certificate Vocational Programme 2022
Link Modules Examination

Common Level

Wednesday 4 May   Morning 10:00 - 12:30

130 marks

Examination Number

Day and Month of Birth

For example, 3rd February
is entered as 0302

INSTRUCTIONS TO CANDIDATES

Write your Examination Number in the box on the front cover.

Write all answers into this booklet. There is space for extra work at the end of the booklet. If you need to use it, make sure to label the work clearly with the question number and part.

This examination booklet will be scanned and your work will be presented to an examiner on screen. Anything that you write outside of the answer areas may not be seen by the examiner.

There are **three** sections in this examination, as follows:

Section A – Audio Visual

There are eight questions. Answer **all eight** of them.   30 marks

Section B – Case Study and Section C – General Questions   100 marks

Answer Section B and **any three** questions from Section C

or

Answer **any four** questions from Section C.

You may only use blue or black pen when writing your answers. Do not use pencil.

Section A	Audio Visual	30 marks

- You will have **three** minutes to read the questions in Section A.
- You will be shown a DVD with Corporate Social Responsibility (CSR) as the theme.
- You will see the DVD **three** times.
  - The first showing will include the whole sequence.
  - It will then be shown in **three** parts. After each part is shown, you will be given time to write your answers in the appropriate section of the answer book.
  - You will then see the entire DVD sequence again.

Answer all **eight** questions on the pages that follow. This page may be used for notes.

Part 1

Q.1 Name **one** benefit of doing a group project. **(1 mark)**

Q.2 Name **two** tourism jobs in the Kilabbey area. **(2 marks)**

Q.3 What are the aims of Corporate Social Responsibility (CSR)? **(3 marks)**

Part 2

Q.4 Describe how CSR affects employees in this supermarket. **(2 marks)**

Q.5 Explain the value of CSR to a business. **(4 marks)**

Q.6 In your opinion which of the four areas of CSR is more important? Give reasons for your answer.   **(6 marks)**

Community ☐   Workplace ☐   Environment ☐   Marketplace ☐

Part 3

Q.7 Do you agree with Bríd that customers are prepared to pay more for something?
Justify your answer.

(6 marks)

[blank ruled answer space]

Q.8 Bríd says that CSR is a win:win for all involved. Do you agree with her? Give **three** reasons for your answer. **(6 marks)**

Section B – Case Study and Section C – General Questions

100 marks: 4 x 25 marks

Answer Section B and **any three** questions from Section C

or

Answer **any four** questions from Section C.

Alex and Rami both worked in the retail sector for many years. In 2015, having identified a gap in the market for young fashion, they set up their own shop selling a number of popular clothing fashion brands. They rented a premises on the main street of a busy large town which meant they had plenty of passing trade. As with many businesses such as theirs, overheads, including rent and wages for four full-time staff were quite high. However, after five years of hard work, the business was doing so well they were thinking of expanding - setting up a second shop diversifying into accessories and footwear.

Then the COVID-19 pandemic happened. During the first lockdown in March 2020 everything closed down. At that point, Alex and Rami found themselves with a lot of stock and more on the way from suppliers. These clothes were already paid for but now there were no customers to sell them to. As the shop had only a very basic online presence, their loyal customers had no option but to shop elsewhere online if they wanted to buy clothes. Having reviewed their current situation, the partners decided to research what their competitors were doing. They discovered that in order for their business to survive they needed to establish an online presence.

Alex and Rami sought help from their Local Enterprise Office (LEO) with a view to creating an online shop promoting their clothes to potential customers in the virtual world. Through the Government's National Digital Strategy, they were eligible for the Trading Online Voucher Scheme. They used their voucher to pay for the design and development of their website and social media accounts. They invested in photography and video equipment in order to take professional quality photographs and videos. They also set up a secure payment system and adopted a transparent and fair returns policy.

On their online platforms, Alex and Rami wrote clear product descriptions, issued daily updates and carried out weekly fashion shows. They made themselves available by email, chat and phone in order to answer queries from customers and to offer personal style advice. They contacted a couple of well-known personalities to become influencers for their online shop promoting their clothes and generating sales. Soon their dedication and innovation paid off and the orders started to come in.

Six months post-lockdown online sales have overtaken shop sales. They are now looking to hire new staff in the areas of website development and maintenance, product promotion, digital marketing and cyber security. Other local businesses having seen their success have asked Alex to mentor them, whilst Rami looks after the day to day running of the business.

Given the success of the diversification of the business into online sales they have updated their business objectives to include business consultancy. Alex and Rami are seriously considering not renewing their lease on the shop premises in 6 months' time in order to concentrate on the online business.

Answer **all three** questions.

Q.1 Describe **three** ways in which Alex and Rami have shown themselves to be enterprising.

(6 marks)

Q.2 (i) Describe **one** reward and **one** risk associated with diversification.

(ii) Write the job description for **one** new member of staff now needed by this enterprise.

(iii) Write the person specification for this new staff member which describes the attributes, skills, qualifications and experience which Alex and Rami would like this person to have.

(9 marks)

Q.3 **(i)** Why would a business carry out a SWOT/SCOT analysis?

(ii) Contrast selling online with selling in-person.

(iii) Why do you think Alex and Rami were successful diversifying into online sales?

(10 marks)

14

Section B – Case Study and Section C – General Questions

100 marks: 4 x 25 marks

Answer Section B and **any three** questions from Section C

or

Answer **any four** questions from Section C.

This section has seven questions. Each question carries 25 marks.

To help you decide which questions to answer and to help you find them in the booklet, here are all the questions with the page range for each. Answer your chosen questions in the appropriate pages in this booklet.

Q.1   **Pages 18 to 20**

A fashion show is an example of an LCVP enterprise activity to raise funds for a local charity.

(a)   Name **four** items for the agenda of the first meeting to be held to plan the fashion show.

(b)   Outline why planning is important in setting up and running this enterprise activity.

(c)   Set out the section of the Enterprise/Action Plan which deals with the running of this activity.

(d)   A dispute has arisen among the students in the class about responsibilities. Describe **three** steps that could be taken to resolve this dispute.

Q.2   **Pages 21 to 23**

A career investigation is useful when making a choice about your future career.

(a)   **(i)**   Name the career you would like to investigate.
          (ii)   Outline **three** duties that would be involved in the above named career.

(b)   Describe an out-of-school learning experience you could undertake to help you choose your future career.

(c)   Describe the challenges of undertaking a career investigation.

(d)   During the pandemic many people worked from home. Outline the benefits and challenges for employees of working from home.

Q.3   **Pages 24 to 26**

Teamwork plays a vital role in the majority of LCVP activities.

(a)   What is your understanding of teamwork?

(b)   Describe **two** characteristics of an effective team member.

(c)   How can a team of students ensure they successfully complete an activity?

(d)   Describe **three** ways a team could evaluate its group performance.

Participation in LCVP provides valuable knowledge of the world of work.

(a) Outline **two** non-financial benefits of employment.

(b) Give **two** reasons why an employee needs a clearly defined role in the workplace.

(c) Describe **four** benefits to an employee of being a member of a trade union.

(d) Discuss **three** benefits to employees and employers when a business complies with Health and Safety regulations.

Learning about your local area.

(a) List **four** sources of employment in your local area.

(b) Identify and explain **two** principal economic activities in your area.

(c) What is the value of completing a 'My Own Place' investigation? Give **four** reasons for your answer.

(d) What challenges might your local area face over the next five years? How might these be overcome?

Voluntary organisations enhance the communities they operate in.

(a) **(i)** Name **two** voluntary organisations that provide a service in your area.
(ii) State **two** sources of funding for voluntary organisations.

(b) Explain how a voluntary organisation differs from a commercial business.

(c) Write the email you would send to a local voluntary organisation when seeking volunteer work.

(d) Describe in detail **three** challenges for a new voluntary organisation setting up in your area.

A rigorous recruitment process is essential to select the right candidate for the job.

(a) Why are job applicants asked to submit references or to name referees on their CV?

(b) List **four** pieces of advice you would give to a friend when filling out a job application form.

(c) Describe **four** ways you would prepare for a job interview, stating why in each case.

(d) **(i)** What preparation should an interviewer do prior to an interview?
(ii) Why is it necessary for an interviewer to have good interviewing skills?

Q.1   **25 marks**

A fashion show is an example of an LCVP enterprise activity to raise funds for a local charity.

(a)   Name **four** items for the agenda of the first meeting to be held to plan the fashion show.

(4 marks)

(b)   Outline why planning is important in setting up and running this enterprise activity.

(4 marks)

18

(c) Set out the section of the Enterprise/Action Plan which deals with the running of this activity.

(8 marks)

(d) A dispute has arisen among the students in the class about responsibilities. Describe **three** steps that could be taken to resolve this dispute.

(9 marks)

20

Q.2 **25 marks**

A career investigation is useful when making a choice about your future career.

(a) **(i)** Name the career you would like to investigate.
 (ii) Outline **three** duties that would be involved in the above named career.

(4 marks)

(b) Describe an out-of-school learning experience you could undertake to help you choose your future career. **(4 marks)**

(c) Describe the challenges of undertaking a career investigation.

(8 marks)

(d) During the pandemic many people worked from home. Outline the benefits and challenges for employees of working from home. **(9 marks)**

Q.3   **25 marks**

Teamwork plays a vital role in the majority of LCVP activities.

(a)   What is your understanding of teamwork?

                                                                              (4 marks)

(b)   Describe **two** characteristics of an effective team member.

                                                                              (4 marks)

(c) How can a team of students ensure they successfully complete an activity?

(8 marks)

25

(d) Describe **three** ways a team could evaluate its group performance.

(9 marks)

Participation in LCVP provides valuable knowledge of the world of work.

(a) Outline **two** non-financial benefits of employment.

(4 marks)

(b) Give **two** reasons why an employee needs a clearly defined role in the workplace.

(4 marks)

(c) Describe **four** benefits to an employee of being a member of a trade union.

(8 marks)

(d) Discuss **three** benefits to employees and employers when a business complies with Health and Safety regulations.

(9 marks)

Q.5   **25 marks**

Learning about your local area.

(a)   List **four** sources of employment in your local area.

                                                                                                  (4 marks)

(b)   Identify and explain **two** principal economic activities in your area.

                                                                                                  (4 marks)

(c) What is the value of completing a 'My Own Place' investigation? Give **four** reasons for your answer. **(8 marks)**

(d) What challenges might your local area face over the next five years? How might these be overcome?

(9 marks)

Q.6 	**25 marks**

Voluntary organisations enhance the communities they operate in.

(a) 	**(i)** 	Name **two** voluntary organisations that provide a service in your area.

	(ii) 	State **two** sources of funding for voluntary organisations.

	(4 marks)

(b) 	Explain how a voluntary organisation differs from a commercial business.

	(4 marks)

(c) Write the email you would send to a local voluntary organisation when seeking volunteer work. **(8 marks)**

(d) Describe in detail **three** challenges for a new voluntary organisation setting up in your area.

(9 marks)

Q.7   **25 marks**

A rigorous recruitment process is essential to select the right candidate for the job.

(a) Why are job applicants asked to submit references or to name referees on their CV?

(4 marks)

(b) List **four** pieces of advice you would give to a friend when filling out a job application form.

(4 marks)

(c)   Describe **four** ways you would prepare for a job interview, stating why in each case.

(8 marks)

(d) **(i)** What preparation should an interviewer do prior to an interview?

(ii) Why is it necessary for an interviewer to have good interviewing skills?

(9 marks)

You may use this page for extra work.

Make sure to label extra work clearly with the question number and part.

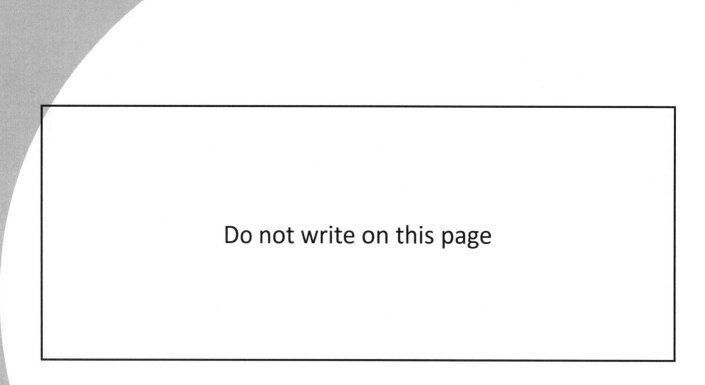

Do not write on this page

Leaving Certificate Vocational Programme – Common Level

Link Modules Examination

Wednesday 4 May

Morning 10:00 - 12:30

Coimisiún na Scrúduithe Stáit

State Examinations Commission

Leaving Certificate Vocational Programme 2021

Link Modules Examination

Common Level

Saturday 8 May   Morning 10:00 – 12:30

Examination Number

Day and Month of Birth

For example, 3rd February
is entered as 0302

Centre Stamp

INSTRUCTIONS TO CANDIDATES

Write your Examination Number in the box on the front cover.

Write all answers into this booklet. There is space for extra work at the end of the booklet. If you need to use it, make sure to label the work clearly with the question number and part.

This examination booklet will be scanned and your work will be presented to an examiner on screen. Anything that you write outside of the answer areas may not be seen by the examiner.

There are **three** sections in this examination, as follows:

Section A – Audio Visual

There are eight questions. Answer **all eight** of them.   30 marks

Section B – Case Study and Section C – General Questions   100 marks

Answer Section B and **any three** questions from Section C

or

Answer **any four** questions from Section C.

You may only use blue or black pen when writing your answers. Do not use pencil.

- You will have **three** minutes to read the questions in Section A.
- You will be shown a DVD with interviewing for a job as the theme.
- You will see the DVD **three** times.
  - The first showing will include the whole sequence.
  - It will then be shown in **three** parts. After each part is shown, you will be given time to write your answers in the appropriate section of the answer book.
  - You will then see the entire DVD sequence again.

Answer all **eight** questions on the pages that follow. This page may be used for notes.

Part 1

Q.1 Name **one** way a job may be advertised. **(1 mark)**

Q.2 What preparation did Mark do for this interview? **(2 marks)**

Q.3 What preparation did Kate do for this Zoom interview? **(3 marks)**

Part 2

Q.4 Why would Mark prefer the hotel trainee program to a college course as his chosen career path? Give **two** reasons. **(2 marks)**

Q.5 Describe how Mark's research benefited him in the interview. **(4 marks)**

Q.6 People are born with qualities but can learn skills.

(i) Name and explain **one** skill and **one** quality that Mark shows in his interview.

(ii) Which of these might be more important to Kate for this particular job?
Give **one** reason for your answer. **(6 marks)**

Part 3

Q.7 Why is it important for a hotel employee to be able to handle a conflict situation?

(6 marks)

Q.8 (i) Why is a scoring sheet essential when conducting an interview?

(ii) Do you agree with Kate's evaluation that Mark is a very strong candidate for this trainee programme? Give reasons for your answer.

(6 marks)

Section B – Case Study and Section C – General Questions

100 marks: 4 x 25 marks

Answer Section B and **any three** questions from Section C

or

Answer **any four** questions from Section C.

Grosvenor Hotel

The Grosvenor Hotel is a small family run business situated in a historic town on the Wild Atlantic Way. The hotel has 45 bedrooms, a function room that can hold up to 200 people, a small dining room and a bar which hosts live music. The hotel employs 40 people, many of the staff are local to the town itself and have worked at the hotel for many years. The hotel supports the local community and economy. During the summer tourist season extra part-time staff are employed in the bar, kitchen and housekeeping sections of the hotel.

Up until recently the Grosvenor Hotel was the only hotel in the town. However, an international chain of hotels has received planning permission to build a state of the art hotel on the outskirts of the town. This hotel will be open for the coming tourist season. It will have 150 bedrooms, a ballroom which can hold up to 300 people, a restaurant and a bar. It will also have a swimming pool, leisure centre and a spa.

The owners of the Grosvenor Hotel are very concerned about the new hotel and the impact it will have on their business. They decided to commission a report from a business consultant who specialises in the travel and tourism sector. He conducted extensive market research to identify their target market and to establish ideas for diversification.

Once the data from the market research was analysed the business consultant met with the owners to discuss the report. He reminded them that while they are a small hotel they can use this as their unique selling point. He outlined some of the positives, for example, the character and history of the hotel, the personal attention the guests receive and the location of the hotel. A number of negative factors were also highlighted; the dated décor in some of the rooms and accessibility for guests with disabilities.

The owners reflected on the report, prioritised a number of the recommendations and drew up a business plan. They realised they needed to invest money in the hotel to bring all the bedrooms up to the same standard. As the hotel is an old Georgian building they have arranged for a visit from the National Disability Authority to advise them on the changes they need to undertake to make it more accessible for people with disabilities.

Rebranding the hotel and creating a new logo was another area that required both attention and investment. The owners decided to update their website and establish a presence on social media. They contacted Fáilte Ireland for advice and assistance with marketing and promoting the hotel. Creating mutually beneficial partnerships with the local community and local businesses was another recommendation from the business consultant. The owners reached out to the local golf club and water sports centre as they realise activity holidays are very popular with tourists. The owners invested their personal savings along with securing a business loan from their local bank to finance the project. With a limited budget and time frame the owners set about safeguarding the future of their hotel.

Answer **all three** questions.

Q.1 Explain **three** of the following terms

(i) Market research
(ii) To invest

(iii) Diversification
(iv) Unique selling point

(6 marks)

Q.2 **(i)** Why is a business plan important when securing finance?

(ii) Set out the marketing section of the business plan used by the owners to secure the bank loan. Use **three** relevant headings.

(9 marks)

Q.3 **(i)** What challenges exist, other than competition, for businesses? How might these challenges be overcome?

(ii) Describe the benefits to the Grosvenor Hotel from the mutually beneficial partnerships with the local community and local businesses.

(10 marks)

54

Section B – Case Study and Section C – General Questions

100 marks: 4 x 25 marks

Answer Section B and **any three** questions from Section C

or

Answer **any four** questions from Section C.

This section has seven questions. Each question carries 25 marks.

To help you decide which questions to answer and to help you find them in the booklet, here are all the questions with the page range for each. Answer your chosen questions in the appropriate pages in this booklet.

Q.1   **Pages 58 to 60**

Learning about a local business/organisation – visit out/visit in.

(a)   Describe how your class would decide on which business/organisation to study.

(b)   Outline **three** benefits of teamwork in this LCVP activity.

(c)   Describe **four** factors important to the success or failure of a visit out/visit in.

(d)   **(i)** List the headings that would be included in a summary report of this activity.
              (ii) What is the value of completing a summary report? Give **three** reasons.

Q.2   **Pages 61 to 63**

Work experience/shadowing is an important first step into the world of work.

(a)   **(i)**   Identify an employer/placement where you would like to do work experience.
              (ii)   List **two** reasons why you chose this employer to carry out your work
                          experience/shadowing.

(b)   Write the email you would send when seeking a work experience/shadowing placement.

(c)   Outline **three** legal responsibilities that employers have when employing workers under
              18 years of age.

(d)   Describe **three** ways the work experience/shadowing placement can help you in school and
              in your future career.

Q.3   **Pages 64 to 66**

My Own Place develops an understanding of the area you live in.

(a)   Name **four** key areas that should be investigated in order to understand the area you live in.

(b)   Outline **two** advantages and **two** disadvantages of using a questionnaire as a method of
              gathering information.

(c)   A group in your local area wants to improve facilities for young people. Design the
              questionnaire this group would use to carry out the research.

(d)   Describe the benefits to a community when different organisations come together to work
              on a project.

Q.4   **Pages 67 to 69**

Ireland has embraced diversity in the workplace.

(a)   What is meant by diversity in the workplace?

(b)   Explain what is meant by equal opportunities in the workplace.

(c)   Outline the advantages for a business that values diversity in the workplace.

(d)   Outline the steps an employee can take if they have a dispute in the workplace.

Q.5   **Pages 70 to 72**

Entrepreneurs are essential for the economy.

(a)   State **four** methods a business enterprise could use to generate ideas.

(b)   Explain how the role of an entrepreneur differs from that of a manager in a business.

(c)   Communication skills, time management skills, decision-making skills and creative skills are
        some of the skills associated with successful entreprenuers. Explain why **three** of these skills
        are important for entrepreneurs.

(d)   (i)   Why is evaluation important to a business?
        (ii)   Discuss **three** areas entrepreneurs could look at in order to evaluate their enterprises.

Q.6   **Pages 73 to 75**

Effective leadership is essential for organisations to be successful.

(a)   Why do organisations need a leader?

(b)   Outline the personal characteristics that make leaders effective.

(c)   Describe **four** ways an organisation can ensure its employees remain motivated.

(d)   Describe **three** challenges facing an organisation as a result of poor leadership.

Q.7

A business wants to expand into online sales.   **Pages 76 to 78**

(a)   Give **two** reasons why a business would move to selling online.

(b)   Outline the supports available to business owners wishing to develop their business.

(c)   State and explain **three** key items that should be included in a funding application when
        seeking finance for business development.

(d)   Describe in detail **three** challenges for a business that wants to move to online sales.

Q.1   **25 marks**

Learning about a local business/organisation – visit out/visit in.

(a)   Describe how your class would decide on which business/organisation to study.

(2 marks)

(b)   Outline **three** benefits of teamwork in this LCVP activity.   **(6 marks)**

(c) Describe **four** factors important to the success or failure of a visit out/visit in.

(8 marks)

(d) **(i)** List the headings that would be included in a summary report of this activity.

(ii) What is the value of completing a summary report? Give **three** reasons.

(9 marks)

Work experience/shadowing is an important first step into the world of work.

(a)   **(i)**   Identify an employer/placement where you would like to do work experience.

(ii)   List **two** reasons why you chose this employer to carry out your work experience/shadowing.   **(4 marks)**

(b)   Write the email you would send when seeking a work experience/shadowing placement.

(6 marks)

(c) Outline **three** legal responsibilities that employers have when employing workers under 18 years of age. **(6 marks)**

(d) Describe **three** ways the work experience/shadowing placement can help you in school and in your future career.
(9 marks)

Q.3   **25 marks**

My Own Place develops an understanding of the area you live in.

(a)   Name **four** key areas that should be investigated in order to understand the area you live in.

                                                                             (4 marks)

(b)   Outline **two** advantages and **two** disadvantages of using a questionnaire as a method of gathering information.   **(4 marks)**

(c) A group in your local area wants to improve facilities for young people. Design the questionnaire this group would use to carry out the research. **(8 marks)**

(d) Describe the benefits to a community when different organisations come together to work on a project. **(9 marks)**

Q.4   **25 marks**

Ireland has embraced diversity in the workplace.

(a)   What is meant by diversity in the workplace?   **(4 marks)**

(b)   Explain what is meant by equal opportunities in the workplace.

(4 marks)

(c) Outline the advantages for a business that values diversity in their workplace.

(8 marks)

(d) Outline the steps an employee can take if they have a dispute in the workplace.

(9 marks)

Q.5   **25 marks**

Entrepreneurs are essential for the economy.

(a)   State **four** methods a business enterprise could use to generate ideas.

                                                                           (4 marks)

(b)   Explain how the role of an entrepreneur differs from that of a manager in a business.

                                                                           (6 marks)

(c) Communication skills, time management skills, decision-making skills and creative skills are some of the skills associated with successful entrepreneurs. Explain why **three** of these skills are important for entrepreneurs.

(6 marks)

(d) **(i)** Why is evaluation important to a business?

(ii) Discuss **three** areas entrepreneurs could look at in order to evaluate their enterprises.

(9 marks)

Q.6   **25 marks**

Effective leadership is essential for organisations to be successful.

(a)   Why do organisations need a leader?   **(4 marks)**

(b)   Outline the personal characteristics that make leaders effective.

(4 marks)

(c) Describe **four** ways an organisation can ensure its employees remain motivated.

(8 marks)

(d) Describe **three** challenges facing an organisation as a result of poor leadership.

(9 marks)

Q.7   **25 marks**

A business wants to expand into online sales.

(a)   Give **two** reasons why a business would move to selling online.

                                                                                                    (4 marks)

```



```

(b)   Outline the supports available to business owners wishing to develop their business.

                                                                                                    (6 marks)

```



```

(c) State and explain **three** key items that should be included in a funding application when seeking finance for business development. **(6 marks)**

(d) Describe in detail **three** challenges for a business that wants to move to online sales.

(9 marks)

You may use this page for extra work.

Make sure to label extra work clearly with the question number and part.

Do not write on this page

Leaving Certificate Vocational Programme – Common Level

Link Modules Examination

Saturday 8 May

Morning 10:00 – 12:30

Coimisiún na Scrúduithe Stáit
State Examinations Commission

Leaving Certificate Vocational Programme 2020

Link Modules Examination

Common Level

2 hours 30 minutes

160 marks

Examination Number

Day and Month of Birth

For example, 3rd February
is entered as 0302

Centre Stamp

INSTRUCTIONS TO CANDIDATES

Write your Examination Number in the box on the front cover.

Write all answers into this booklet. There is space for extra work at the end of the booklet. If you need to use it, make sure to label the work clearly with the question number and part.

This examination booklet will be scanned and your work will be presented to an examiner on screen. Anything that you write outside of the answer areas may not be seen by the examiner.

You may only use blue or black pen when writing your answers. Do not use pencil.

There are **three** sections in this examination, as follows.

Section A – Audio Visual

There are eight questions. Answer **all eight** of them.   30 marks

Section B – Case Study

There are three questions. Answer **all three** of them.   30 marks

Section C – General Questions

There are six questions. Answer **any four** of them.   100 marks

- You will have **three** minutes to read the questions in Section A.
- You will be shown a DVD about Committee Meetings.
- You will see the DVD **three** times.
  - The first showing will include the whole sequence.
  - It will then be shown in **three** parts. After each part is shown, you will be given time to write your answers in the appropriate section of the answer book.
  - You will then see the entire DVD sequence again.

Answer all **eight** questions on the pages that follow. This page may be used for notes.

2020

PART 1

Q.1 What evidence is there that Denise is environmentally aware? **(1 mark)**

Q.2 What is the goal of the committee? **(2 marks)**

Q.3 Describe **three** actions identified by the committee in its plan. **(3 marks)**

PART 2

Q.4 Explain what it means to take 'minutes' at a meeting.

(3 marks)

Q.5 Aside from taking minutes, describe the other responsibilities of the secretary of a committee.

(4 marks)

Q.6 **(i)** What are the aims of this first meeting?

(ii) What evidence is there that this committee is achieving these aims?

(5 marks)

PART 3

Q.7 **(i)** Describe the characteristics of a good committee member?

(ii) Is it important to have all young people on a committee? Give reasons for your answer.

(6 marks)

Q.8 **(i)** Describe the differences between a well run committee meeting and a badly run committee meeting.

(ii) Describe **two** responsibilities of a chairperson of a committee.　　　**(6 marks)**

Climate Entrepreneur

In June 2019, the Government of Ireland launched the Climate Action Plan to address the impacts of the climate emergency on Ireland's environment, society, economic and natural resources. Jim, a resident of Ballyglas, recently attended a meeting of his Local Community Group which has recently joined the Sustainable Energy Community Network and is working on an Energy Master Plan in partnership with Sustainable Energy Authority Ireland (SEAI).

While sitting at this meeting, Jim realised that there were business opportunities involved in increasing the energy efficiency in homes. He learned that a key aim of the *Climate Action Plan* is to reduce Ireland's dependency on fossil fuels. To achieve this, the installation of oil boilers will be banned by 2022 and gas boilers by 2025. In order to move from fossil fuels to renewable energy heating systems, 600,000 heat pumps will be installed by 2030, of which 400,000 will be retrofitted into existing buildings.

Jim has worked as a qualified plumber for the last ten years. He enjoyed the job security that came with being an employee but has always aspired to setting up his own business one day. He believes he has the necessary skills to become an entrepreneur. After the meeting, he researched the new air to water heat pumps. He researched their sources, costs and installation criteria. He discovered he would need to upskill himself in order to meet the SEAI criteria to register as someone who can install heat pumps. He visited a house that had recently installed an air to water heat pump and spoke with the owners regarding their experience of this heating system. He met with a Technical Advisor from SEAI who recommended that Jim would attend a SEAI workshop on renewable energy heating systems.

Jim made an appointment with the Local Enterprise Office to discuss the risks, challenges and benefits of setting up his own company. He was assigned a business mentor who discussed the different options for establishing himself as a sole-trader, a partnership or setting up a public limited company. He learned about professional indemnity; employers insurance; health and safety legislation. They discussed location, staff requirements and promoting his business.

Jim's mentor made him realise that preparation is the single most important thing he could do to ensure his business gets off the ground. His mentor suggested that Jim should sign up to the Local Enterprise Office *Start Your Own Business* programme. This programme guides potential entrepreneurs through the various aspects of business planning. In particular, Jim should attend the module dealing with basic bookkeeping as this is something he is not familiar with.

Jim decided he was willing to take a risk and launched *Jim's Green Heating*. He invested his personal savings in the business along with securing a small business loan from his local bank. Initially, he decided that he would set up as a sole-trader with a view to expansion if the business grows.

Answer **all three** questions.

Q.1 Explain **three** of the following terms. (6 marks)

(i) mentor   **(iii)** sole trader
(ii) bookkeeping   **(iv)** upskill

Q.2 **(i)** Describe **three** key pieces of essential research Jim carried out when considering setting up his own business.

(ii) Describe **three** ways Jim could promote his business and give an advantage of each method chosen.

2020

(12 marks)

Q.3 (i) Describe the importance to the success of the business of **three** of the topics discussed by Jim with the mentor, other than promoting his own business.

(ii) Describe **three** reasons why Jim was successful in securing the business loan from the bank.

(12 marks)

This section has six questions. Each question carries 25 marks. Answer any **four** questions.

To help you decide which questions to answer and to help you find them in the booklet, here are all the questions with the page range for each. Answer your four chosen questions in the appropriate pages in this booklet.

Q.1   **Pages 96 to 98**

Manray Technologies needs to recruit a Technical Solutions Engineer. The following job advertisement appeared on the company's website.

Technical Solutions Engineer required for a full-time position

The successful applicant must possess a Bachelor's Degree in Computer Science. They should have excellent troubleshooting, <u>problem solving</u>, written and verbal communication skills. We are offering an attractive salary and <u>flexible working hours</u>.

Please apply with CV including two <u>referees</u> to hr@manraytechnologies.ie. Manray Technologies is an <u>equal opportunities employer</u>.

www.manraytechnologies.ie

(a)   Explain **two** of the underlined terms.

(b)   State **four** pieces of information that should be included in a Contract of Employment.

(c)   Describe **four** reasons why this employer wants an employee with excellent communication skills.

(d)   As part of the interview process you are expected to give a presentation to the employer.
        (i)   Outline **three** areas that should be included in this presentation.
        (ii)   How can you make your presentation stand out from those by other interviewees?

Q.2   **Pages 99 to 101**

Entrepreneurs are the driving force for jobs in Ireland.

(a)   **(i)**   Explain the term 'entrepreneur'.
        (ii)   Name **two** necessary qualities of an entrepreneur.

(b)   Why should entrepreneurs keep up-to-date with new technologies? Give **two** reasons.

(c)   Describe the advantages and the disadvantages of being self-employed.

(d)   Discuss in detail **three** factors which may cause a business to fail.

Work Experience/Work Shadowing is a vital part of the LCVP.

(a) What further preparation would you carry out having secured your work experience/work shadowing placement?

(b) Explain **three** personal goals you had in relation to your work experience/work shadowing.

(c) Explain **three** responsibilities of employees with regard to Health and Safety in the workplace.

(d) **(i)** Describe **three** challenges that a student may experience during their work experience/work shadowing.

      (ii) Outline how these challenges might be overcome.

You have been asked to complete an investigation on a career of your choice.

(a) (i) Name the career you chose and outline **one** benefit to you from undertaking this investigation.

      (ii) Name **two** methods of research you used to investigate your career.

(b) Describe **three** reasons why you would chose one entry pathway into a career over another.

(c) Describe **three** ways in which you as an employee can demonstrate a strong work ethic.

(d) Employers require a dynamic workforce to compete in today's business world. Describe **three** benefits to the employer when they employ highly skilled and educated employees.

A visit in from a guest speaker.

(a) **(i)** Outline the benefits of inviting a guest speaker to address the LCVP class.

      (ii) Name **one** Leaving Certificate subject you are studying other than Link Modules and outline how it was useful in the organisation/planning of your visit in.

(b) Describe **three** reasons why teamwork is so important to the success of this activity.

(c) Draft an email to brief the guest speaker in advance of the visit to your LCVP class.

(d) Describe **four** methods that could be used to evaluate the visit in and give reasons for each method chosen.

Planning for a business start-up

(a) List **four** sources of finance for a business start-up.

(b) Outline **three** reasons for preparing a business plan.

(c) Describe how the success of a business enterprise can be measured.

(d) **(i)** State and explain **three** key items that should be included in the body of a business plan.

      (ii) Outline why each of these three items is important.

Q.1 (25 marks)

Manray Technologies needs to recruit a Technical Solutions Engineer. The following job advertisement appeared on the company's website.

Technical Solutions Engineer required for a full-time position

The successful applicant must possess a Bachelor's Degree in Computer Science. They should have excellent troubleshooting, <u>problem solving</u>, written and verbal communication skills.

We are offering an attractive salary and <u>flexible working hours</u>.

Please apply with CV including two <u>referees</u> to hr@manraytechnologies.ie.

Manray Technologies is an <u>equal opportunities employer</u>.

www.manraytechnologies.ie

(a) Explain **two** of the underlined terms. **(4 marks)**

| |
| |
| |
| |
| |

(b) State **four** pieces of information that should be included in a Contract of Employment. **(4 marks)**

| |
| |
| |
| |
| |
| |
| |
| |
| |
| |
| |
| |

(c) Describe **four** reasons why this employer wants an employee with excellent communication skills.

(8 marks)

(d) As part of the interview process you are expected to give a presentation to the employer.

    (i) Outline **three** areas that should be included in this presentation.

    (ii) How can you make your presentation stand out from those by other interviewees?

        (9 marks)

Q.2 (25 marks)

Entreprenuers are the driving force for jobs in Ireland.

(a) **(i)** Explain the term 'entrepreneur'.
    (ii) Name **two** necessary qualities of an entrepreneur. (4 marks)

(b) Why should entrepreneurs keep up-to-date with new technologies? Give **two** reasons.
(4 marks)

(c) Describe the advantages and the disadvantages of being self-employed.

(8 marks)

(d) Discuss in detail **three** factors which may cause a business to fail.

(9 marks)

Q.3 **(25 marks)**

Work Experience/Work Shadowing is a vital part of the LCVP.

(a) What further preparation would you carry out having secured your work experience/work shadowing placement? **(4 marks)**

(b) Explain **three** personal goals you had in relation to your work experience/work shadowing. **(6 marks)**

(c) Explain **three** responsibilities of employees with regard to Health and Safety in the workplace.

(6 marks)

(d) **(i)** Describe **three** challenges that a student may experience during their work experience/work shadowing.

(ii) Outline how these challenges might be overcome. **(9 marks)**

Q.4   **(25 marks)**

You have been asked to complete an investigation on a career of your choice.

(a) **(i)** Name the career you chose and outline **one** benefit to you from undertaking this investigation.

   (ii) Name **two** methods of research you used to investigate your career.   **(4 marks)**

(b) Describe **three** reasons why you would chose one entry pathway into a career over another.

                                                                                                         (6 marks)

(c)   Describe **three** ways in which you as an employee can demonstrate a strong work ethic.

(6 marks)

(d) Employers require a dynamic workforce to compete in today's business world. Describe **three** benefits to the employer when they employ highly skilled and educated employees.

(9 marks)

Q.5 (25 marks)

A visit in from a guest speaker.

(a) (i) Outline the benefits of inviting a guest speaker to address the LCVP class.
(ii) Name **one** Leaving Certificate subject you are studying other than Link Modules and outline how it was useful in the organisation/planning of your visit in.

(3 marks)

(b) Describe **three** reasons why teamwork is so important to the success of this activity.

(6 marks)

(c) Draft an email to brief the guest speaker in advance of the visit to your LCVP class.

(8 marks)

(d) Describe **four** methods that could be used to evaluate the visit in and give reasons for each method chosen.

(8 marks)

Q.6 **(25 marks)**

Planning for a business start-up.

(a) List **four** sources of finance for a business start-up. **(4 marks)**

(b) Outline **three** reasons for preparing a business plan. **(6 marks)**

(c) Describe how the success of a business enterprise can be measured.

(6 marks)

112

(d) **(i)** State and explain **three** key items that should be included in the body of a business plan.

(ii) Outline why each of these three items is important.

(9 marks)

Do not write on this page

Leaving Certificate Vocational Programme – Common Level

Link Modules Examination

2 hours 30 minutes

13877

Coimisiún na Scrúduithe Stáit
State Examinations Commission

2019

Leaving Certificate Vocational Programme 2019

Link Modules Examination

Wednesday 1 May   Morning 10:00 – 12:30

Examination number					

INSTRUCTIONS TO CANDIDATES

Write your Examination Number in the box on the front cover.

Write all answers into this booklet. There is space for extra work at the end of the booklet. If you need to use it, make sure to label the work clearly with the question number and part.

This examination booklet will be scanned and your work will be presented to an examiner on screen. Anything that you write outside of the answer areas may not be seen by the examiner.

There are **three** sections in this examination, as follows.

Section A – Audio Visual

There are eight questions. Answer **all eight** of them.   30 marks

Section B – Case Study

There are three questions. Answer **all three** of them.   30 marks

Section C – General Questions

There are six questions. Answer **any four** of them.   100 marks

You may only use blue or black pen when writing your answers. Do not use pencil.

- You will have **three** minutes to read the questions in Section A.
- You will be shown a DVD with an Apprenticeship theme.
- You will see the DVD **three** times.
  - The first showing will include the whole sequence.
  - It will then be shown in **three** parts. After each part is shown, you will be given time to write your answers in the appropriate section of the answer book.
  - You will then see the entire DVD sequence again.

Answer all **eight** questions on the pages that follow. This page may be used for notes.

PART 1

Q.1 Who told Pádraig about the Apprenticeship information evening? **(1 mark)**

Q.2 Why does Anna think an apprenticeship in Aircraft Mechanics would suit Pádraig? **(2 marks)**

Q.3 Who will be involved in the information evenings? **(3 marks)**

PART 2

Q.4 Why did Anna decide to do an apprenticeship? **(4 marks)**

Q.5 **(i)** What is the duration of apprenticeship courses?
(ii) What qualification will Anna receive at the end of her course? **(4 marks)**

Q.6   What are the benefits to being an apprentice?   **(4 marks)**

PART 3

Q.7 Why would the apprenticeship programme appeal to a broad range of individuals?

(6 marks)

121
PART 3

Q.8 What are the benefits of an effective apprenticeship programme for an employer?

(6 marks)

122

Ballytiernan Community Co-operative

Ballytiernan is a picturesque village situated on the banks of a river. It is located twenty kilometres from the nearest city and has an adequate bus service. Agriculture is the main economic activity while tourism is also important to the local economy. The village is popular with anglers and has hosted many angling competitions in the past. It has two primary schools and a co-educational community college which offers Post Leaving Certificate (PLC) courses. An active local development group is in existence.

The Local Development Group has been working on concerns raised by anglers about illegal dumping at a number of locations along the banks of the river and in the river. The group is afraid this could ruin the reputation of the town as a clean and beautiful area.

A farm set on fifty acres of land at the edge of the town was bequeathed to the community of Ballytiernan by a local farmer. His express wish was that the farm should be used for the benefit of the community and in particular to teach young people the art of horticulture, gardening and sustainable animal husbandry. He had always been an advocate for sustainable and ethical business practices. The farm has been given to the Local Development Group to manage.

The Local Development Group in Ballytiernan formed the Ballytiernan Community Co-operative (Co-op) to manage the 50 acre farm. Its aim is to establish community based enterprises operating from the farm site. It has received assistance from the County Council, The Irish Co-operative Organisation Society, and Teagasc. The Co-op runs the farm itself, using organic and sustainable farming practices. It has established a farm shop which sells farm produce and local crafts and a café which uses locally sourced produce. Space is available for other appropriate local enterprises.

The farm is also being used by Leaving Certificate students and college students, particularly those doing courses in agriculture and horticulture for work experience and to complete the practical components of their courses. Allotments have been created which the local community can use for a small fee.

A large tract of land has been designated for use by local clubs, schools and organisations. The local Foróige club and the Men's Shed group have already been using the farm buildings. Schools in the area have been invited to submit proposals / plans for how they would use the designated land.

The Co-Op is aware of the huge potential of the site both for the local and the extended community and it has drawn up a plan to manage current projects. The Co-op is also assessing the economic viability of a number of projects, including glamping in luxury yurts, a weekend music festival and an open farm.

Answer **all three** questions.

Q.1 Describe **three** advantages that the Ballytiernan area enjoys. **(6 marks)**

Q.2 **(i)** What benefits does the Local Development Group bring to the area?

(ii) Outline what assistance the Co-Op might receive from state agencies.

(iii) Why does the Co-Op need this assistance? **(12 marks)**

2019

Q.3 One of the local schools is interested in using the land.
   (i) Name a suitable enterprise for the site. Explain why.
   (ii) Outline the proposal or plan they would submit to the co-op.
      Set out your proposal or plan under **three** headings.   **(12 marks)**

This section has six questions. Each question carries 25 marks. Answer any **four** questions.

To help you decide which questions to answer and to help you find them in the booklet, here are all the questions with the page range for each. Answer your four chosen questions in the appropriate pages in this booklet.

Q.1   **Pages 130 – 132**

The world of work is dynamic and diverse.

(a) What is a Curriculum Vitae (CV) used for? List **three** headings which should be included on a CV.

(b) State and explain **three** personal skills/qualities that help to make a job applicant more employable.

(c) Outline **three** legal responsibilities that employers have when employing workers under 18 years of age.

(d) Upskilling courses are offered to those seeking work.
    (i) Explain what is meant by the term 'upskilling'.
    (ii) How does the participant benefit from these courses?

Q.2   **Pages 133 – 135**

Your Link Modules class has been asked to co-ordinate an enterprise activity selling hoodies to the Leaving Certificate students of your school.

(a) List **three** methods of idea generation for a class enterprise activity.

(b) **(i)** Explain what is meant by the term 'market research'.
    (ii) Explain why market research is necessary for this activity.

(c) Design a questionnaire to carry out market research for this enterprise activity. It should contain at least **five** questions.

(d) **(i)** Why is it important to evaluate this enterprise activity?
    (ii) State and explain **three** methods which can be used to evaluate this activity.

Q.3   **Pages 136 – 138**

Teamwork is an essential part of the LCVP.

(a) **(i)** Name **one** LCVP team activity you participated in.
    (ii) Describe your role in this activity.

(b) Prepare the agenda for the first meeting to plan and organise the activity stated above.

(c) Outline **three** characteristics of an effective team member.

(d) While organisations place an emphasis on teamwork it can also create challenges.
    (i) Describe **three** challenges of teamwork.
    (ii) Outline how these challenges may be overcome.

Q.4   Pages 139 – 141

A visit to a local business enterprise.

(a)   Name the business enterprise your class visited and describe **two** reasons why you chose this particular business enterprise.

(b)   Outline **four** steps that should be taken in preparation for this visit.

(c)   Describe **four** key areas of information you were informed about during this visit.

(d)   Does the LCVP prepare students with the skills they need to succeed in the modern world of work?   Give **three** reasons for your answer.

Q.5   Pages 142 – 144

Voluntary organisations play a valuable role in our society.

(a)   **(i)**   What is the purpose of voluntary organisations?
         (ii)   Name **two** voluntary organisations in your area.

(b)   You would like to work in a voluntary organisation. To ensure that you do a good interview, what preparation would you carry out in advance?

(c)   Describe **three** ways a local community benefits from the existence of a voluntary organisation.

(d)   Name **three** challenges facing voluntary organisations. Describe how these challenges can be overcome.

Q.6   Pages 145 – 147

Information and Communication Technology (ICT) is the driving force of the world of work in the 21st century.

(a)   Name **four** ways you have used ICT during the LCVP.

(b)   Why are ICT skills necessary for an employee in today's working environment?

(c)   Describe how ICT could be used effectively by a business.

(d)   Discuss **three** challenges that affect organisations and businesses that use ICT.

Q.1 *The world of work is dynamic and diverse.* **(25 marks)**

(a) What is a Curriculum Vitae (CV) used for? List **three** headings which should be included on a CV.

(4 marks)

(b) State and explain **three** personal skills/qualities that help to make a job applicant more employable. **(6 marks)**

(c) Outline **three** legal responsibilities that employers have when employing workers under 18 years of age.

(6 marks)

(d) Upskilling courses are offered to those seeking work.
 (i) Explain what is meant by the term upskilling.
 (ii) How does the participant benefit from these courses? **(9 marks)**

Q.2 (25 marks)

Your Link Modules class has been asked to co-ordinate an enterprise activity selling hoodies to the Leaving Certificate students of your school.

(a) List **three** methods of idea generation for a class activity. (3 marks)

(b) **(i)** Explain what is meant by the term 'market research'.
(ii) Explain why market research is necessary for this activity. (5 marks)

(c) Design a questionnaire to carry out market research for this enterprise activity. It should contain at least **five** questions.

(8 marks)

(d) **(i)** Why is it important to evaluate this enterprise activity?

(ii) State and explain **three** methods which can be used to evaluate this activity.

(9 marks)

Q.3 *Teamwork is an essential part of the LCVP.* **(25 marks)**

(a) **(i)** Name **one** LCVP team activity you participated in.
(ii) Describe your role in this activity. **(4 marks)**

(b) Prepare the agenda for the first meeting to plan and organise the activity stated above.
(6 marks)

(c) Outline **three** characteristics of an effective team member. **(6 marks)**

(d) While organisations place an emphasis on teamwork it can also create challenges.

  (i) Describe **three** challenges of teamwork.

  (ii) Outline how these challenges may be overcome. **(9 marks)**

Q.4 A *visit to a local business enterprise.* **(25 marks)**

(a) Name the business enterprise your class visited and describe **two** reasons why you chose this particular business enterprise. **(3 marks)**

(b) Outline **four** steps that should be taken in preparation for this visit. **(8 marks)**

(c) Describe **four** key areas of information you were informed about during this visit.

(8 marks)

(d) Does the LCVP prepare students with the skills they need to succeed in the modern world of work? Give **three** reasons for your answer.

(6 marks)

141

Q.5 *Voluntary organisations play a valuable role in our society.* **(25 marks)**

(a) **(i)** What is the purpose of voluntary organisations?
(ii) Name **two** voluntary organisations in your area. **(4 marks)**

(b) You would like to work in a voluntary organisation. To ensure that you do a good interview, what preparation would you carry out in advance? **(6 marks)**

(c) Describe **three** ways a local community benefits from the existence of a voluntary organisation.

(9 marks)

(d) Name **three** challenges facing voluntary organisations. Describe how these challenges can be overcome.

(6 marks)

Q.6 *Information and Communications Technology (ICT) is the driving force of the world of work in the 21st century.* **(25 marks)**

(a) Name **four** ways you have used ICT during the LCVP. **(4 marks)**

2019

(b) Why are ICT skills necessary for an employee in today's working environment? **(4 marks)**

(c) Describe how ICT could be used effectively by a business. **(8 marks)**

(d) Discuss **three** challenges that affect organisations and businesses that use ICT. **(9 marks)**

2019

You may use this page for extra work.

Make sure to label extra work clearly with the question number and part.

You may use this page for extra work.

Make sure to label extra work clearly with the question number and part.

2019

Leaving Certificate Vocational Programme – Common Level

Link Modules

Wednesday 1 May
Morning 10:00 – 12:30

Coimisiún na Scrúduithe Stáit

State Examinations Commission

Leaving Certificate Vocational Programme

Link Modules Examination 2018

Wednesday, 2 May 2018, 10.00 – 12.30

2018

Examination Number

For examiner use only

Written paper		
		mark
Section A		
Section B		
Section C	Q.1	
	Q.2	
	Q.3	
	Q.4	
	Q.5	
	Q.6	
Total		

Portfolio	
	mark
1	
2	
3	
4	
5	
6	
7	
8	
Total	

Cumulative tot check – written	
1. Final end-of-page total	
2. Sum of disallowed questions	
3. Total awarded (1 minus 2)	

Cumulative tot check – portfolio	
1. Total marks	
2. Sum of disallowed items	
3. Total awarded (1 minus 2)	

INSTRUCTIONS TO CANDIDATES

Write your Examination Number in the box on the front cover.

Write all answers into this booklet. There is space for extra work at the end of the booklet. If you need to use it, make sure to label the work clearly with the question number and part.

There are **three** sections in this examination, as follows.

Section A – Audio Visual

There are eight questions. Answer **all eight** of them.   **(30 marks)**

Section B – Case Study

There are three questions. Answer **all three** of them.   **(30 marks)**

Section C – General Questions

There are six questions. Answer **any four** of them.   **(100 marks)**

- You will have **three** minutes to read the questions in Section A.
- You will be shown a DVD with a Business Location theme.
- You will see the DVD **three** times.
  - The first showing will include the whole sequence.
  - It will then be shown in **three** parts. After each part is shown, you will be given time to write your answers in the appropriate section of the answer book.
  - You will then see the entire DVD sequence again.

Answer all **eight** questions on the pages that follow. This page may be used for notes.

_____

_____

_____

_____

_____

_____

_____

_____

_____

_____

_____

_____

_____

_____

_____

_____

_____

_____

2018

PART 1

Q.1 What is the name of Evan's business?   **(1 mark)**

_____

_____

_____

Q.2 As well as product, what other elements does Evan consider important in becoming a successful business?   **(2 marks)**

_____

_____

_____

_____

_____

_____

Q.3 What influenced Evan in his decision on where to set up his workshop?   **(3 marks)**

_____

_____

_____

_____

_____

_____

_____

_____

_____

_____

Q.4 What reasons does Evan give for sponsoring the local gaelic football team?   **(4 marks)**

_____

_____

_____

_____

_____

_____

_____

_____

_____

_____

_____

_____

_____

_____

2018

Q.5 List the benefits of doing a feasibility study?   **(4 marks)**

_____

_____

_____

_____

_____

_____

_____

_____

_____

_____

_____

Q.6 Evan is an innovative business person. What evidence is there to support this statement? **(4 marks)**

_____

_____

_____

_____

_____

_____

_____

_____

_____

_____

_____

_____

_____

_____

_____

_____

_____

_____

_____

_____

_____

Q.7 What has Evan learned from his self-evaluation of the business? **(6 marks)**

Q.8 What evidence is there that Evan is aware of the positive impact of IT on a business. How can he ensure that IT development continues to be beneficial? **(6 marks)**

Section B   **Case Study**   **30 marks**

VOLUNTEERING

Many communities rely on volunteers to help deliver services and programmes that enhance the life of the people living in the area. Local Volunteer Centres were set up to help match those who needed volunteer workers with individuals offering their services. The Volunteer Centres offer advice, placement and support services to individuals and organisations who are interested in volunteering in Ireland.

Opportunities also exist for those who wish to have the experience of volunteering abroad. Tailored volunteer projects are offered by many agencies.

People volunteer for a variety of reasons. In Tommy's case, having spent most of his working life in the construction industry, he found himself unemployed for a long period of time after his employer went out of business. He was becoming increasingly concerned about the challenges of gaining new employment. During a visit to his local Intreo Office he learned that he could volunteer and his jobseekers allowance would not be affected. Tommy decided to contact his local Volunteer Centre to explore some volunteering opportunities. This would give him the opportunity to develop new skills and gain valuable experience for his CV.

Sarah is a Placement Officer in the Volunteer Centre; she matches organisations that need help with people who wish to volunteer. Tommy had a face-to-face meeting with Sarah during which she pointed out a number of things Tommy should consider if he wishes to volunteer while searching for a job. Volunteering is a great way to improve his chances of finding work but it is important not to let it interfere with his job search. Tommy discovered there are a number of aspects he should consider before committing to volunteering if his experience of being a volunteer is to be a positive one.

Having registered with the Volunteer Centre, Tommy applied for work and secured a placement volunteering at a local care home for the elderly. His decision to accept this placement is due to his personal engagement with care homes. His elderly father has been living in a state-of-the-art facility for the last 6 months. Through his experience in the care home Tommy realised that this type of work really suited him. He researched the qualifications that are required for this career and he applied to do a course in Care Skills at a Further Education College.

Many organisations depend greatly on the positive impact of volunteering. Companies give back to society through their Corporate Social Responsibility strategy. Given the differences between commercial and volunteer organisations, it is important to ensure effective structures exist. Larger companies appoint Volunteer Co-ordinators who play a vital and varied role for both the individual and the organisation. Experience has shown that involving all parties in decision-making is vital to the success of volunteer agencies in Ireland.

2018

Answer **all three** questions.

Q.1 Explain **three** of the following terms
  (i)   Volunteer
  (ii) Construction Industry
  (iii) Placement Officer
  (iv) Corporate Social Responsibility.

(6 marks)

_____

_____

_____

_____

_____

_____

_____

_____

_____

_____

_____

_____

_____

_____

_____

_____

_____

_____

_____

_____

_____

_____

Q.2

(i) What might have influenced Tommy when choosing where to volunteer? What might Tommy gain from volunteering?

(ii) Outline the steps in the recruitment process when an organisation is looking for a volunteer.
(12 marks)

Q.3

(i) Compare and contrast a voluntary body with a commercial business.

(ii) What challenges exist for a new voluntary body setting up in your area. **(12 marks)**

2018

Section C General Questions 100 marks

This section has six questions. Each question carries 25 marks. Answer **any four** questions.

To help you decide which questions to answer and to help you find them in the booklet, here are all the questions with the page range for each. Answer your four chosen questions in the appropriate pages in this booklet.

Q.1 Pages 166 – 168

Enterprise is essential for growth in the economy.

(a) Explain what you understand by the term 'enterprise'.

(b) Describe **two** examples of enterprise in action in each of the following.

(i) Household   (ii) Local Community.

(c) Identify **two** agencies which provide support for business start-ups. Outline the type of support offered by each of these agencies.

(d) **Planning, good managerial skills** and **product development** are among the essential elements to ensure continued success for any enterprise. Outline the importance of each.

Q.2 Pages 169 – 171

As part of your LCVP course you are required to undertake work experience/work shadowing which will help you make informed career choices.

(a) Name **one** career you might be interested in and identify **two** skills/qualities required to pursue it.

(b) (i) State **two** methods of finding work experience/work shadowing.

   (ii) Outline **two** advantages for one of the methods you have listed.

(c) Explain **three** reasons why it is helpful for an employee to have a clearly defined role in the workplace.

(d) Describe how your work experience/shadowing has influenced you in your choice of career. Refer to **two** possible career paths, evaluating each.

Q.3 Pages 172 – 174

Your local area has decided to enter the Tidy Towns competition.

(a) List **two** sources of employment in your local area.

(b) Present the SWOT analysis the organising committee would draw-up for your local area.

(c) Outline the steps that should be taken by the local community in preparation for entry to the competition.

(d) Discuss **three** ways the local community will benefit from participation in the Tidy Towns competition.

Q.4

Pages 175 – 177

A positive workplace atmosphere is of benefit to all.

(a) **(i)** Name **two** Trade Unions.

(ii) What is a shop steward?

(b) Outline **four** reasons why an individual might join a trade union?

(c) Explain the benefits to a business of a good industrial relations climate. How might poor industrial relations affect the business?

(d) Describe **three** obligations an employee has regarding health and safety at work.

Q.5

Pages 178 – 180

You are part of your LCVP class committee to plan upcoming activities.

(a) What is the role of the chairperson of a committee?

(b) What skills should a good chairperson have? Explain each of your answers.

(c) Consider a committee in which you have taken part. What might cause it to be less successful?

(d) What recommendations would you give to students planning their first LCVP class activity.

2018

Q.6

Pages 181 – 183

Your LCVP class has been involved in carrying out an enterprise activity.

(a) List **three** methods of generating an idea for a class project.

(b) Explain what is meant by the term 'marketing mix'.

(c) Draft the marketing section you would have included in your report on this activity.

(d) Outline **four** ways your partipication in this activity will benefit you in future employment.

Q.1   **(25 marks)**

Enterprise is essential for growth in the economy.

(a)   Explain what you understand by the term 'enterprise'.

(4 marks)

_____

_____

_____

_____

_____

_____

_____

_____

_____

(b)   Describe **two** examples of enterprise in action in each of the following.
      (i) Household   (ii) Local Community.   **(4 marks)**

_____

_____

_____

_____

_____

_____

_____

_____

_____

_____

_____

_____

(c) Identify **two** agencies which provide support for business start-ups. Outline the type of support offered by each of these agencies. **(8 marks)**

(d) **Planning**, **good managerial skills** and **product development** are among the essential factors to ensuring continued success for any enterprise. Outline the importance of each.

(9 marks)

_____

_____

_____

_____

_____

_____

_____

_____

_____

_____

_____

_____

_____

_____

_____

_____

_____

_____

_____

_____

_____

Q.2 (25 marks)

As part of your LCVP course you are required to undertake work experience/work shadowing which will help you make informed career choices.

(a) Name **one** career you might be interested in and identify **two** skills/qualities required to pursue it. (3 marks)

_____

_____

_____

_____

_____

_____

(b) (i) State **two** methods of finding work experience/work shadowing.
   (ii) Outline **two** advantages for one of the methods you have listed. (5 marks)

_____

_____

_____

_____

_____

_____

_____

_____

_____

_____

_____

_____

_____

_____

_____

(c) Explain **three** reasons why it is helpful for an employee to have a clearly defined role in the workplace.

(9 marks)

_____

_____

_____

_____

_____

_____

_____

_____

_____

_____

_____

_____

_____

_____

_____

_____

_____

_____

_____

_____

_____

(d) Describe how your work experience/shadowing has influenced you in your choice of career. Refer to **two** possible career paths evaluating each. **(8 marks)**

Q.3 (25 marks)

Your local area has decided to enter the Tidy Towns competition.

(a) List **two** sources of employment in your local area. (2 marks)

_____

_____

_____

_____

_____

_____

(b) Present the SWOT analysis the organising committee would draw-up for your local area.

(8 marks)

_____

_____

_____

_____

_____

_____

_____

_____

_____

_____

_____

_____

_____

_____

_____

_____

_____

(c) Outline the steps that should be taken by the local community in preparation for entry to the competition. **(6 marks)**

(d) Discuss **three** ways the local community will benefit from participation in the Tidy Towns competition.

(9 marks)

Q.4   **(25 marks)**

A positive workplace atmosphere is of benefit to all.

(a)   (i)   Name **two** Trade Unions.   **(5 marks)**

     (ii) What is a shop steward?

_____

_____

_____

_____

_____

_____

_____

(b)   Outline **four** reasons why an individual might join a trade union?   **(8 marks)**

_____

_____

_____

_____

_____

_____

_____

_____

_____

_____

_____

_____

_____

_____

2018

(c) Explain the benefits to a business of a good industrial relations climate. How might poor industrial relations affect the business? **(6 marks)**

_____

_____

_____

_____

_____

_____

_____

_____

_____

_____

_____

_____

_____

_____

_____

_____

_____

_____

_____

_____

_____

_____

(d) Describe **three** obligations an employee has regarding health and safety at work.

(6 marks)

Q.5 (25 marks)

You are part of your LCVP class committee to plan upcoming activities.

(a) What is the role of the chairperson of a committee?

(4 marks)

_____

_____

_____

_____

_____

(b) What skills should a good chairperson have? Explain each of your answers. (6 marks)

_____

_____

_____

_____

_____

_____

_____

_____

_____

_____

_____

_____

_____

_____

_____

_____

_____

_____

(c) Consider a committee in which you have taken part. What might cause it to be less successful? **(6 marks)**

(d) What recommendations would you give to students planning their first LCVP class
activity. **(9 marks)**

_____

_____

_____

_____

_____

_____

_____

_____

_____

_____

_____

_____

_____

_____

_____

_____

_____

_____

_____

_____

_____

_____

_____

_____

_____

Q.6 (25 marks)

Your LCVP class has been involved in carrying out an enterprise activity.

(a) List **three** methods of generating an idea for a class project. (3 marks)

_____

_____

_____

_____

_____

_____

(b) Explain what is meant by the term 'marketing mix'. (6 marks)

_____

_____

_____

_____

_____

_____

_____

_____

_____

_____

_____

_____

_____

_____

_____

_____

_____

2018

(c) Draft the marketing section you would have included in your report on this activity.

(8 marks)

(d) Outline **four** ways your partipication in this activity will benefit you in future employment. **(8 marks)**

_____

_____

_____

_____

_____

_____

_____

_____

_____

_____

_____

_____

_____

_____

_____

_____

_____

_____

_____

_____

_____

_____

_____

_____

_____

2018

You may use this page for extra work.
Make sure to label extra work clearly with the question number and part.

Coimisiún na Scrúduithe Stáit

State Examinations Commission

Leaving Certificate Vocational Programme

Link Modules Examination 2017

Wednesday, 3 May 2017, 10.00 – 12.30

2017

INSTRUCTIONS TO CANDIDATES

Write your Examination Number in the box.

Write all answers into this Answer Book.

There are **three** Sections in this Examination.

Examination Number

Section A – Audio Visual

There are **eight** questions.

All questions must be answered. **(30 marks)**

Section B – Case Study

There are **three** questions.

All questions must be answered. **(30 marks)**

Section C – General Questions

There are **six** questions.

Four questions must be answered. **(100 marks)**

Section A	Audio Visual	30 marks

- You will have **three** minutes to read the questions in Section A.
- You will be shown a DVD with a Work Experience theme.
- You will see the DVD **three** times.
  - The first showing will include the whole sequence.
  - It will then be shown in **three** parts. After each part is shown, you will be given time to write your answers in the appropriate section of the answer book.
  - You will then see the entire DVD sequence again.

This page may be used for notes or to supplement answers.

Section A	Audio Visual	30 marks	Office Use Only	
			1	2
Answer all questions.				
Part 1				
Q.1 What type of business is "Play It" productions?				
		1 mark		
Q.2 Where did Emily do an internship?				
		2 marks		
Q.3 Why does Emily like to take on work experience students?				
		3 marks		

Section A	Audio Visual	30 marks	Office Use Only	
			1	2

Part 2

Q.4 What does Cathal see himself doing on work experience?

4 marks

Q.5 Do you believe that Cathal has a realistic career path thought out for himself? Why?

Section A	Audio Visual	30 marks		

Part 2

	1	2

Section A	Audio Visual	30 marks	Office Use Only	
			1	2
		4 marks		
Q.6 Outline the challenges facing businesses, according to Emily.				
Section A	**Audio Visual**	**30 marks**	1	2
		4 marks		

189

Section A	Audio Visual	30 marks	Office Use Only	
			1	2
Part 3				
Q.7 Cathal has asked for feedback on his interview. What feedback would be given to him?				
	6 marks			

Section A	Audio Visual	30 marks	Office Use Only	
Q.8 Evaluate how the work placement experience would benefit Emily as a business owner.			1	2

Section A	Audio Visual			
		6 marks	1	2

Section B	Case Study	30 marks

AMY'S CHOCOLATE

Amy graduated from college with a languages degree and went to work in the marketing department of a large multinational company. She was very successful and was promoted several times. However, after a number of years she felt the need to reassess the direction her career was taking. Amy had always wanted to run her own business and drew on her lifelong hobby of cooking and baking for inspiration. Over the years, she has sold her produce at local country markets. Her chocolate and fudge confectionaries consistently proved most popular. Keen to explore new options, while still working, Amy completed a "Start Your Own Business" evening course which provided her with invaluable insight into running a business.

After extensive market research, she decided to leave her marketing job and embark on a new career, thus "Amy's Chocolate" was established. Initial financial support was provided both by her family and her own savings. Amy decided that working in her home was not a feasible option hence a suitable premises in her local town was found. This new premises allows for both the production and sales of her products on site.

"Amy's Chocolate" has won many awards both for the success of the business and the top quality product itself. Amy has diversified into different areas to develop her business: personalised gifts and hampers, children's chocolate making parties, Easter egg making and decorating etc. She has put a lot of thought and research into her styling, packaging and presentation. Many of her ingredients have been sourced locally, thus supporting the local community and economy. She has recruited staff from a nearby college of further education and trained them in both production and sales. Amy prides herself on her positive approach to staff development. She considers herself and her staff to be a team that works well together ensuring a high quality final product. From the knowledge gained on the "Start Your Own Business" course Amy has come to realise that there are many elements to a successful business and each must be developed and strengthened.

To further increase sales, Amy has approached a large retail outlet offering to supply her speciality chocolate; should she be successful she will have to expand her business. The existing premises would not be adequate to cope with such large orders. In addition, extra staff and equipment would be needed. A unit in a local enterprise centre has become available that would suit the business requirements. Further finance will have to be sourced if the business is to expand. She is presently looking at various options available to her, has started to prepare a new business plan and has talked to two agencies that help and support businesses and entrepreneurs.

Amy has taken full advantage of the opportunities presented to her. She has tailored and personalised her approach to recruitment and training of staff and has been duly rewarded for this. Having built a loyal team, everyone employed by Amy delivers the highest standard of work and of produce thus helping the business reach its goals.

The chocolate market is very competitive and this brings its own challenges. However, despite the hard work related to the management of a business, Amy never regrets moving from being an employee to owning her own business. This career change has given her personal and professional satisfaction despite the risks and challenges involved. Amy has developed new skills and is aware that she must continually develop both personally and professionally to ensure future business success.

Section B	Case Study	30 marks	Office Use Only	
			1	2
Answer all questions.				
Q.1 Name and explain **three** ways Amy may have carried out market research.				
			6 marks	1	2

			1	2
Q.2 (a)	What evidence do we have that shows Amy is innovative in her business?			
(b)	State and explain **three** areas that would have been covered in the "Start Your Own Business" course.			
(c)	What objectives might Amy set in the preparation of her business plan?			
Q.2 (a)	What evidence do we have that shows Amy is innovative in her business?		1	2
(b)	State and explain **three** areas that would have been covered in the "Start Your Own Business" course.			
(c)	What objectives might Amy set in the preparation of her business plan?			

12 marks

Q.3 (a) Explain how the role of entrepreneur differs from that of employee as experienced by Amy.

(b) Outline which areas Amy should focus on into the future to ensure business success.

12 marks		

| Answer **four** questions |

INDEX AND SUMMARY

Section C contains 6 questions of 25 marks each and you should answer **any four**. To assist in deciding and locating the questions to answer, the following is the text of all the questions with the page number range for each. Answer your choice in the appropriate pages that follow in this booklet.

Q.1 The Career Investigation is a core LCVP activity.   **Pages 198 – 200**

- (a) Name a career you have investigated and outline **one** reason why you chose to investigate this career.
- (b) Explain **one** skill and **one** quality you have that make you suitable for this career.
- (c) Outline **four** sources of information you used to investigate this career.
- (d) Describe **three** methods of evaluating your career investigation.

Q.2 Communication and good presentation skills are key in the work place.   **Pages 201 – 203**

- (a) Why is it important to have good communication skills?
- (b) Name and explain **three** methods of communicating in the work place.
- (c) Explain **three** issues which may occur in a business as a result of poor communication skills?
- (d) Consider a class activity in which you were involved where good presentation skills were evident. Describe **three** areas where good presentation skills enhanced the activity.

Q.3 Volunteers play a key role in the delivery of services both locally and nationally.   **Pages 204 – 206**

- (a) Name a voluntary organisation in your local area and outline the type of work they carry out.
- (b) List **three** questions you might ask on a first meeting or visit to a voluntary organisation that you would like to join.
- (c) Discuss what a voluntary organisation will expect from a volunteer. **Four** points should be made.
- (d) State and explain **four** ways you would promote volunteering in your community.

Q.4 Your class is organising a visit-out to a business enterprise in your local area.   **Pages 207 – 209**

- (a) Name the business/enterprise you visited and briefly outline **two** objectives your class has for the proposed visit.
- (b) Outline **three** ways the local community benefit from this business.
- (c) Write a letter to the business requesting permission to visit them.
- (d) Identify and explain the benefits of working as part of a team in this activity.

Q.5 Businesses are committed to employing the best candidate for all their vacancies.   **Pages 210 – 212**

- (a) What does having a good work ethic and being a responsible employee mean?
- (b) List the benefits that are brought to a business when employees have a good work ethic.
- (c) List **six** pieces of information that should be included in a contract of employment given to a new employee.
- (d) Describe in detail **three** important recruitment factors that employers look for in a potential employee.

Q.6 Your class is planning to organise a career exhibition evening in your school.   **Pages 213 – 215**

- (a) Why have a career exhibition?
- (b) Set out, under **three** headings, a plan to organise a career exhibition.
- (c) Outline **four** challenges you and your class might encounter when organising the night.
- (d) Describe **three** ways the success of the career exhibition night could be measured.

Section C	General Questions	100 marks	Office Use Only	
			1	2
Q.1 The Career Investigation is a core LCVP activity.				
(a) Name a career you have investigated and outline **one** reason why you chose to investigate this career.				
	4 marks			
(b) Explain **one** skill and **one** quality you have that make you suitable for this career.				
			1	2

198

4 marks		
(c) Outline **four** sources of information you used to investigate this career.		
8 marks		

(d) Describe **three** methods of evaluating your career investigation.

9 marks

Section C	General Questions	100 marks	Office Use Only	
			1	2
Q.2 Communication and good presentation skills are key in the work place.				
(a) Why is it important to have good communication skills?				
		2 marks		
(b) Name and explain **three** methods of communicating in the work place.				
		6 marks	1	2

(c) Explain **three** issues which may occur in a business as a result of poor communication skills?

9 marks

(d) Consider a class activity in which you were involved where good presentation skills were evident. Describe **three** areas where good presentation skills enhanced the activity.

8 marks

			1	2

Q.3 Volunteers play a key role in the delivery of services both locally and nationally.

(a) Name a voluntary organisation in your local area and outline the type of work they carry out.

3 marks

(b) List **three** questions you might ask on a first meeting or visit to a voluntary organisation that you would like to join.

6 marks

(c) Discuss what a voluntary organisation will expect from a volunteer. **Four** points should be made.

8 marks

(d)   State and explain **four** ways you would promote volunteering in your community.

8 marks

Section C	General Questions	100 marks	Office Use Only	
			1	2

Q.4 **Your class is organising a visit-out to a business enterprise in your local area.**

(a)   Name the business/enterprise you visited and briefly outline **two** objectives your class has for the proposed visit.

3 marks

(b)   Outline **three** ways the local community benefit from this business.

6 marks

(c)   Write a letter to the business requesting permission to visit them.

10 marks

(d)   Identify and explain the benefits of working as part of a team in this activity.

6 marks

2017

Section C	General Questions	100 marks	Office Use Only	
			1	2
Q.5 **Businesses are committed to employing the best candidate for all their vacancies.**				
(a) What does having a good work ethic and being a responsible employee mean?				
		4 marks		
(b) List the benefits that are brought to a business when employees have a good work ethic.				

6 marks

(c) List **six** pieces of information that should be included in a contract of employment given to a new employee.

6 marks

(d) Describe in detail **three** important recruitment factors that employers look for in a
     potential employee.

9 marks

Section C	General Questions	100 marks	Office Use Only	
			1	2

Q.6 Your class is planning to organise a career exhibition evening in your school.

(a) Why have a career exhibition?

2 marks

(b) Set out, under **three** headings, a plan to organise a career exhibition.

6 marks

(c) Outline **four** challenges you and your class might encounter when organising the night.

8 marks

(d) Describe **three** ways the success of the career exhibition night could be measured.

9 marks

For Examiner use only
Written Examination Paper

	Marks Awarded
Section A	
Section B	
Section C	
Q.1	
Q.2	
Q.3	
Q.4	
Q.5	
Q.6	
Total	

Examination No.

1.	Total of end of page totals.	
2.	Aggregate total of all disallowed answers.	
3.	Total marks awarded (1 minus 2).	

Portfolio Assessment

	Marks Awarded
1	
2	
3	
4	
5	
6	
7	
8	
Total	

1.	Total marks.	
2.	Aggregate total of all disallowed items.	
3.	Total marks awarded (1 minus 2).	

Coimisiún na Scrúduithe Stáit

State Examinations Commission

Leaving Certificate Vocational Programme

Link Modules Examination 2016

Wednesday, 4 May 2016, 10.00 – 12.30

INSTRUCTIONS TO CANDIDATES

Write your Examination Number in the box.

Write all answers into this Answer Book.

There are **three** Sections in this Examination.

Examination Number

Section A – Audio Visual

There are **eight** questions.

All questions must be answered.   **(30 marks)**

Section B – Case Study

There are **three** questions.

All questions must be answered.   **(30 marks)**

Section C – General Questions

There are **six** questions.

Four questions must be answered.   **(100 marks)**

Section A	Audio Visual	30 marks

- You will have **three** minutes to read the questions in Section A.
- You will be shown a DVD with a Leadership theme.
- You will see the DVD **three** times.
  - The first showing will include the whole sequence.
  - It will then be shown in **three** parts. After each part is shown, you will be given time to write your answers in the appropriate section of the answer book.
  - You will then see the entire DVD sequence again.

This page may be used for notes or to supplement answers.

Answer all questions.

Part 1

Q.1 What type of product does TechMedPro make?

2 marks

Q.2 What is a Senior Team Leader in TechMedPro expected to do?

2 marks

Q.3 Why does Siobhán consider herself to be a competent employee?

2 marks

2016

Section A	Audio Visual	30 marks	Office Use Only	
			1	2
Part 2				
Q.4 Explain why Siobhán believes her leadership style is effective.				
4 marks				
Q.5 Why is motivation from within considered more beneficial to employees?				

4 marks

Q.6 Explain some of the ways Siobhán could motivate her team to perform better.

4 marks

2016

Part 3

Q.7 Outline the differences between a manager and a leader.

6 marks

Section A	Audio Visual	30 marks	Office Use Only	
			1	2
Q.8 Explain the reasons why it is important for TechMedPro to provide appropriate staff training in relation to feedback in the workplace.				
	6 marks		1	2

2016

GLENOR COMMUNITY PROJECT

Glenor is a small picturesque town of approximately two thousand inhabitants. It is located 80km from a large city and approximately 30km from three larger towns. Glenor's Development Committee is a very active and progressive organisation and has been involved in community development for many years. All stakeholders work tirelessly on issues that matter to them. More recently, due to increased optimism in the local economy, the committee has tried to focus on more innovative ways to increase the town's prosperity.

Ratlow Forest Park is nearby, set in the scenic foot hills of Glenor and covers approximately 1,200 hectares. In recent years Glenor's Development Committee has been busy developing this wonderful park which now includes 20km of looped walking trails of varying degrees of difficulty. A modern children's playground and a picnic area are in close proximity to the park. The Cuan River stretches the full length of the park and is used for angling and offers the possibility of being used for water sports. The committee believes Glenor's natural resources can be used to the area's advantage.

Glenor's Development Committee has successfully completed a town improvement project including replacing old inefficient street lighting with new ornate poles incorporating high efficiency light bulbs. Also, new hanging baskets and large richly planted flower pots have been added to enhance the ambiance of the town. This improvement work has helped to transform the town in many ways resulting in it being a recent winner of a National Tidy Towns Award.

The upsurge of general goodwill in recent years has resulted in considerable financial gains as is evident from the increased income generated from tourism. However, there is still scope to improve this further. Presently, members of the committee are developing a website and a smart phone app for the town. Both the website and app will contain all the information that a visitor may require about Glenor. These developments will be of huge benefit to visitors and residents alike.

Glenor's Development Committee plans to maximise the use of the area's vast natural resources. Recently, a meeting of all interested stakeholders was held and from the discussions both a short and long-term project were identified. The 'Glenor Active Challenge 2016' was decided on as an achievable short-term project. This will be open to walkers and runners alike and will involve tracks ranging from easy to highly challenging, thus allowing for the full use of Rathlow Park. The committee can apply for grant aid which will provide funding to purchase necessary safety equipment and undertake marketing and promotional campaigns. Negotiations are still underway as to whether mobile catering should be allowed in the park during this event. Effective forward planning and consultation, with communities who have overseen similar projects, is fundamental. It is hoped that large numbers of people will be attracted to the town and, if successful, it is envisaged that it could become an annual event.

Having spoken to groups in other regions experienced in community development, local residents and businesses, the committee realises that the future success of the area lies in the appropriate development of local amenities and natural resources. Consequently, after much enthusiastic debate a "Tree Top Adventure Walk" was agreed as a potential long-term project. This will involve doing a SWOT analysis, a feasibility study and long-term planning. All stakeholders will be involved in the planning and delivery of this new initiative. Both visitors and residents are looking forward to experiencing the rural environment in this new and innovative manner. The Development Committee realise that the future prosperity of the town is contingent on its ability to attract and manage investment while continuing to develop the town as a competitive tourist and recreational destination.

Section B	Case Study	30 marks	Office Use Only	
			1	2
Answer all questions.				
Q.1 List **three** stakeholders that could be involved in Glenor's Development Committee.				
	6 marks		1	2

Section B	Case Study	30 marks	Office Use Only	

Q.2 (a) Consider one of the stakeholders mentioned in Q1.
    (i) Outline what benefits he/she can bring to the committee.
    (ii) Give **two** benefits to this stakeholder of becoming involved with the committee.
(b) State and explain **three** benefits the development committee's work brings to the area.
			1	2

Q.2 (a) Consider one of the stakeholders mentioned in Q1.				

Section B	Case Study	30 marks	Office Use Only	
			1	2
		12 marks		

Q.3
(a) Why does the committee need to develop a plan for the long-term project?
(b) Identify **one** other possible project that could be developed. How would you evaluate its short and long term success?

12 marks

INDEX AND SUMMARY

Section C contains 6 questions of 25 marks each and you should answer **any four**. To assist in deciding and locating the questions to answer, the following is the text of all the questions with the page number range for each. Answer your choice in the appropriate pages that follow in this booklet.

Q.1 **Entrepreneurs are enterprising people and are essential in today's society.** Pages 230 – 232

    (a) (i)   Name an entrepreneur known to you.
        (ii)   Explain the term "enterprising".
    (b)   Outline **three** characteristics of an entrepreneur.
    (c)   Discuss **three** reasons why an entrepreneur would start his/her own business.
    (d)   Describe **four** challenges an entrepreneur might encounter when setting up his/her own business.

Q.2 **As an LCVP class you have decided to wash cars for the local community as an enterprise activity to raise funds for a local charity. You have purchased all the materials you will need for this project.**
Pages 233 – 235

    (a)   List **four** methods you will use to advertise your fundraising activity.
    (b)   Other than the purchased materials outline **three** other aspects of the enterprise you should plan for.
    (c)   Explain **three** benefits to you and the students who have participated in this activity.
    (d)   Discuss **three** methods you will use to evaluate the success of this activity.

Q.3 **Participation in LCVP work experience/work shadowing gives you an invaluable insight into the world of work.** Pages 236 – 238

    (a)   Outline **two** ways work experience/work shadowing differs from school work.
    (b)   Identify **three** outcomes for you from participating in work experience/work shadowing placement.
    (c)   Discuss **three** benefits to employees and employers when a business complies with the Safety, Health & Welfare at Work Act.
    (d)   Write out the evaluation you completed for your work experience/work shadowing placement.

Q.4 **Choco Ltd needs to recruit an Accounts Manager. The following is the job advertisement for the position (page 23).** Pages 239 – 241

    (a)   State **four** ways Choco Ltd could advertise the position.
    (b)   Explain **two** of the words underlined in the advertisement.
    (c)   Choco Ltd. has received 400 applications for this position. Explain how applicants could ensure that their application form, CV and covering letter would stand-out.
    (d)   Discuss how shortlisted applicants can prepare themselves before the interview, on the day of the interview and be prepared for the interview itself.

Q.5 **As an LCVP class you are planning to organise a visitor in from a local voluntary group. You have been asked to plan a meeting to start organising this activity.** Pages 242 – 244

    (a)   List **three** steps you should take to organise this meeting.
    (b)   Draw up an agenda for the first meeting of your class group.
    (c)   Explain **three** reasons why planning in advance for your visit-in is so important.
    (d) (i)   Why is it important for the speaker to have good presentation skills?
        (ii)   How can he/she ensure the presentation is effective?

Q.6 **Consider a local business enterprise in your area.** Pages 245 – 247

    (a)   Name a business enterprise in your local area and give a brief outline of the product/service they provide.
    (b)   Why do you think this enterprise has located itself in your locality?
    (c)   Explain **three** ways the success of this business enterprise could be measured.
    (d)   Discuss **three** reasons why education and training are important to business enterprises.

2016

Section C	General Questions	100 marks	Office Use Only	
			1	2

Q.1 **Entrepreneurs are enterprising people and are essential in today's society.**

(a)   (i)   Name an entrepreneur known to you.

     (ii)   Explain the term "enterprising".

5 marks

(b)   Outline **three** characteristics of an entrepreneur.

6 marks		

(c) Discuss **three** reasons why an entrepreneur would start his/her own business.

6 marks		

2016

(d) Describe **four** challenges an entrepreneur might encounter when setting up his/her own business.

8 marks

Section C	General Questions	100 marks	Office Use Only	
			1	2

Q.2 As an LCVP class you have decided to wash cars for the local community as an enterprise activity to raise funds for a local charity. You have purchased all the materials you will need for this project.

(a) List **four** methods you will use to advertise your fundraising activity.

4 marks

(b) Other than the purchased materials outline **three** other aspects of the enterprise you should plan for.

6 marks		
(c) Explain **three** benefits to you and the students who have participated in this activity.		
6 marks		

(d)   Discuss **three** methods you will use to evaluate the success of this activity.

9 marks

2016

Section C	General Questions	100 marks	Office Use Only	
			1	2
Q.3 **Participation in LCVP work experience/work shadowing gives you an invaluable insight into the world of work.**				
(a) Outline **two** ways work experience/work shadowing differs from school work.				
		4 marks		
(b) Identify **three** outcomes for you from participating in work experience/work shadowing placement.				
			1	2
		6 marks		

(c) Discuss **three** benefits to employees and employers when a business complies with the Safety, Health & Welfare at Work Act.

6 marks

(d) Write out the evaluation you completed for your work experience/work shadowing placement.

9 marks

Section C	General Questions	100 marks	Office Use Only	
			1	2

Q.4 Choco Ltd needs to recruit an Accounts Manager. The following is a job advertisement for the position.

ACCOUNTS MANAGER REQUIRED
For a full-time position.
The successful applicant should have three years post qualification experience in a similar position. They should be proficient in computers, be hardworking and have good <u>interpersonal skills.</u>
Interested candidates should send their CV, <u>covering letter</u> and any <u>references</u> to the <u>Personnel Manager</u> before 06 June, 2016
Choco Ltd, Unit 2, Freeways Business Centre, Dublin 4.
Tel: 01-082 1716   Email: chocopersonnel@eircom.net
Choco Ltd is an equal opportunities employer.

(a) State **four** ways Choco Ltd could advertise this position.

4 marks

(b) Explain **two** of the words underlined in the advertisement.

239

6 marks		

(c) Choco Ltd has received 400 applications for this position. Explain how applicants could ensure that their application form, CV and covering letter would stand-out.

6 marks		

(d) Discuss how the shortlisted applicants can prepare themselves before the interview, on the day of the interview and be prepared for the interview itself.

9 marks

Section C	General Questions	100 marks	Office Use Only	
			1	2
Q.5 As an LCVP class you are planning to organise a visitor in from a local voluntary group. You have been asked to plan a meeting to start organising this activity.				
(a) List **three** steps you should take to organise this meeting.				
		3 marks		
(b) Draw up an agenda for the first meeting of your class group.				
			1	2

8 marks		
(c) Explain **three** reasons why planning in advance for your visit-in is so important.		
6 marks		

(d)   (i)   Why is it important for the speaker to have good presentation skills?
     (ii)   How can he/she ensure the presentation is effective?

8 marks

Section C	General Questions	100 marks	Office Use Only	
			1	2
Q.6	**Consider a local business enterprise in your area.**			
(a)	Name a business enterprise in your local area and give a brief outline of the product/service they provide.			
	4 marks			
(b)	Why do you think this enterprise has located itself in your locality?			
	6 marks			

(c) Explain **three** ways the success of this business enterprise could be measured.

6 marks

(d)   Discuss **three** reasons why education and training are important to business enterprises.

9 marks

For Examiner use only
Written Examination Paper

	Marks Awarded
Section A	
Section B	
Section C	
Q.1	
Q.2	
Q.3	
Q.4	
Q.5	
Q.6	
Total	

Examination No.

1.	Total of end of page totals.	
2.	Aggregate total of all disallowed answers.	
3.	Total marks awarded (1 minus 2).	

Portfolio Assessment

	Marks Awarded
1	
2	
3	
4	
5	
6	
7	
8	
Total	

1.	Total marks.	
2.	Aggregate total of all disallowed items.	
3.	Total marks awarded (1 minus 2).	

Coimisiún na Scrúduithe Stáit

State Examinations Commission

Leaving Certificate Vocational Programme

Link Modules Examination 2015

Wednesday, 6 May 2015, 10.00 – 12.30

INSTRUCTIONS TO CANDIDATES

Write your examination number in the box.

Write all answers into this answer book.

There are **three** sections in this examination.

Examination Number

Section A – Audio Visual

There are **eight** questions.

All questions must be answered.   **(30 marks)**

Section B – Case Study

There are **three** questions.

All questions must be answered.   **(30 marks)**

Section C – General Questions

There are **six** questions.

Four questions must be answered.   **(100 marks)**

2015

Section A	Audio Visual	30 marks

- You will have **three** minutes to read the questions in Section A.
- You will be shown a DVD with an enterprise theme.
- You will see the DVD **three** times.
  - The first showing will include the whole sequence.
  - It will then be shown in three parts. After each part is shown, you will be given time to write your answers in the appropriate section of the answer book.
  - You will then see the entire DVD sequence again.

This page may be used for notes or to supplement answers.

Section A	Audio Visual	30 marks	Office Use Only	
			1	2

Answer all questions.

Part 1

Q.1 What type of business did Sylvia initially want to set up?

                                                                    1 mark

Q.2 Why was this type of business suited to Sylvia?

                                                                    2 marks

Q.3 State the niche market identified by Sylvia as a result of her feasibility study. Outline why this market might be successful for Sylvia.

                                                                    3 marks

			1	2
Part 2				

Q.4 What has Sylvia learned from her previous experience in running a business?

4 marks

Q.5 Explain the types of support the Local Enterprise Office could offer Sylvia.

Section A	Audio Visual	30 marks	Office Use Only	
			1	2
		4 marks		

Q.6 Outline the potential problems that need to be resolved before Sylvia can proceed with her business idea.

	4 marks	1	2

Section A	Audio Visual	30 marks	Office Use Only	
			1	2

Part 3

Q.7 Seán was critical of some aspects of Sylvia's business plan. Explain the importance of a business plan. Suggest how Sylvia could improve her business plan for the next meeting with Seán.

Part 3

6 marks

Section A	Audio Visual	30 marks	Office Use Only	
Q.8 Explain the benefits of the Mentoring Programme offered by the Local Enterprise Office.			1	2

6 marks

2015

Recruit Me Ltd

Robert and Maria Nolan established a recruitment agency, Recruit Me Ltd, in 1998. The company is well known and respected in the recruitment industry in Ireland. The main office is located in Dublin but there are also six sub offices throughout the country. The company has been quite successful. However, the economic downturn has had a very serious impact on the business. The core business for Recruit Me Ltd is recruitment for four large multinational companies. Robert and Maria know that in order to survive, a major change of direction is required. A restructuring programme within the company has just been completed. Employees were offered voluntary redundancy packages and job sharing opportunities. Having reduced the workforce the task of reinventing the company began in earnest. A meeting of the senior management team was held to assess the situation and to discuss the future direction of the company. A SWOT analysis of the business was conducted. There were very detailed discussions of new ideas and ways to diversify in the new economic environment. This led to the development of a new business plan and mission statement.

Corporate Social Responsibility (CSR) is a business practice which involves participating in initiatives that benefit society. Recruit Me Ltd has always had a very strong CSR programme. To further their CSR strategy they have decided to try to meet the needs of a new type of jobseeker in the Irish market i.e. the professional, skilled person, who having been employed for many years, is now struggling to find work. To achieve this, Recruit Me Ltd has introduced a free Careers Programme, provided by staff volunteers, which is available to jobseekers one day each week. They provide a range of services including, developing a professional profile, preparing a CV and practising successful interview techniques. They also offer free employment search and job matching supports.

Another potential growth area identified by Recruit Me Ltd is a programme to assist other companies to develop a CSR strategy. While output and profitability continue to be priorities for any successful company, the stakeholders in those companies also need to deliver a level of social responsibility which will impact on business practice. Recruit Me Ltd will emphasise to these companies that a CSR strategy will require consultation with staff and with the local community, as well as environmental awareness. Significantly, working conditions for employees, recruitment procedures, training and promotion practices and people management need to recognise the importance of fairness, equality of opportunity and the value of all types of work including volunteer work.

Recruit Me Ltd has also taken the opportunity to offer support for new start-up enterprises. With excess space available in their offices, they now offer fully serviced desks for a nominal rent. It is a professional space where entrepreneurs have access to printing, broadband and communication facilities, while being surrounded by likeminded people. Recruit Me Ltd offer these fledgling businesses support in accessing grants from government agencies, as well as dealing with the legal and tax implications of starting a business. It is hoped that once these businesses are established they will move to their own premises and employ more workers. Recruit Me Ltd believes that even though this aspect of the business is currently non-profit making it should generate more clients for them in the future.

Robert and Maria believe that the strategy of diversification has had a huge impact on themselves, their employees and their company. They were prepared to take measured risks and to make a commitment to change. They saw the value of drawing on innovation and creativity within the company. They consider that their action plan for job creation is a positive way to help society. The highly effective, talented and committed team at Recruit Me Ltd, led by Robert and Maria, have weathered the worst of the downturn in the economy. Because of their visionary leadership and the supports they have given to employees, individuals and other companies they have been nominated for a national social entrepreneur's award.

social entrepreneurs
IRELAND

Section B	Case Study	30 marks	Office Use Only	
			1	2
Answer all questions.				

Q.1 Based on your reading of this case study explain **three** of the following terms:
- Mission Statement
- Stakeholders
- Equality of opportunity
- Entrepreneur
- CV

6 marks

2015

Section B	Case Study	30 marks	Office Use Only	
Q.2 (i) Explain the term 'Corporate Social Responsibility' (CSR). (ii) Outline a corporate social responsibility policy implemented by Robert and Maria in Recruit Me Ltd. (iii) Outline the areas that Recruit Me Ltd would recommend for inclusion in a corporate social responsibility strategy for another company.			1	2
Section B	Case Study	30 marks	Office Use Only	

Section B	Case Study	30 marks	Office Use Only	
			1	2
	12 marks			

Q.3 (i) Explain the term 'diversification' as used in the case study.
(ii) Discuss the reasons why it is important for a business to diversify.

12 marks		

Answer **four** questions

INDEX AND SUMMARY

Section C contains six questions of 25 marks each and you should answer **any four**. To assist in deciding and locating the questions to answer, the following is the text of all the questions with the page number range for each. Answer your choice in the appropriate pages that follow in this booklet.

Q.1 **Planning is an essential element to the success of any activity**. **Pages 262 – 264**

    (a) Name and give a brief outline of an LCVP activity that involved planning.
    (b) Explain **three** benefits of planning for this activity.
    (c) Outline **three** different research methods used to obtain the necessary information for this activity.
    (d) Discuss **three** methods used to evaluate this activity.

Q.2 **Voluntary bodies carry out an important role in our local communities**. **Pages 265 – 267**

    (a) (i) Name a local voluntary body in your area.
        (ii) Explain the term 'volunteer'.
    (b) Explain how a local voluntary body differs from a commercial business.
    (c) Outline **four** ways a local community benefits from the presence of a voluntary body in the area.
    (d) Explain the ethical obligations of volunteers when working for a voluntary body.

Q.3 **Work experience/work shadowing gives you an important insight into the world of work**.
                                                                                        Pages 268 – 270
    (a) State **three** methods of finding a work placement.
    (b) Write a letter to an employer of your choice requesting a three day work placement.
    (c) Explain **three** characteristics that make a person more employable.
    (d) Describe **three** ways your participation in work experience has prepared you for the working world.

Q.4 **Well regulated businesses have an impact on employers, employees and the environment**.
                                                                                        Pages 271 – 273
    (a) (i) What is a trade union?
        (ii) Name **two** trade unions.
    (b) Outline **four** benefits of being a member of a trade union.
    (c) (i) Explain a contract of employment.
        (ii) Identify **four** items which should be included in a contract of employment.
    (d) Describe **three** responsibilities of an employer in relation to health and safety regulations.

Q.5 **You have been asked to complete an investigation on a career of your choice**. **Pages 274 – 276**

    (a) What is a career investigation?
    (b) (i) Name a career you investigated.
        (ii) List the steps that could be used to investigate this career.
    (c) State **two** Leaving Certificate subjects required for this career.
        Explain the relevance of these subjects to your career choice.
    (d) Describe **two** pathways into your chosen career using suitable headings.

Q.6 **Your LCVP class has decided to set up a new Loom Band enterprise to raise funds for a local charity**.
                                                                                        Pages 277 – 279
    (a) List **four** methods of idea generation.
    (b) Questionnaires will be used as part of the market research for this product.
        (i) What is market research?
        (ii) Identify **three** methods, other than a questionnaire, used as market research tools.
    (c) Explain **four** disadvantages of using a questionnaire as a market research tool.
    (d) Describe how Information and Communications Technology (ICT) could be used effectively in this enterprise.

Section C	General Questions	100 marks	Office Use Only	
			1	2

Q.1 Planning is an essential element to the success of any activity.

(a) Name and give a brief outline of an LCVP activity that involved planning.

4 marks

(b) Explain **three** benefits of planning for this activity.

6 marks

(c)   Outline **three** different research methods used to obtain the necessary information for this activity.

6 marks

(d)   Discuss **three** methods used to evaluate this activity.

9 marks

9 marks

Section C	General Questions	100 marks	Office Use Only	
			1	2
Q.2 Voluntary bodies carry out an important role in our local communities.				
(a) (i) Name a local voluntary body in your area. (ii) Explain the term 'volunteer'.				
		3 marks		
(b) Explain how a local voluntary body differs from a commercial business.				
		6 marks		

2015

(c) Outline **four** ways a local community benefits from the presence of a voluntary body in the area.

8 marks

(d)   Explain the ethical obligations of volunteers when working for a voluntary body.

8 marks

2015

Section C	General Questions	100 marks	Office Use Only	
			1	2
Q.3	**Work experience/work shadowing gives you an important insight into the world of work.**			
(a)	State **three** methods of finding a work placement.			
	3 marks			
(b)	Write a letter to an employer of your choice requesting a three day work placement.			
Q.3			1	2

10 marks		
(c) Explain **three** characteristics that make a person more employable.		

6 marks		

(d) Describe **three** ways your participation in work experience has prepared you for the working world.

6 marks		

Section C	General Questions	100 marks	Office Use Only	
			1	2
Q.4 **Well regulated businesses have an impact on employers, employees and the environment.**				
(a) (i) What is a trade union? (ii) Name **two** trade unions.				
		5 marks		
(b) Outline **four** benefits of being a member of a trade union.				

2015

8 marks

(c)   (i)   Explain a contract of employment.

       (ii)   Identify **four** items which should be included in a contract of employment.

(d) Describe **three** responsibilities of an employer in relation to health and safety regulations.

2015

Section C	General Questions	100 marks	Office Use Only	
			1	2

Q.5 **You have been asked to complete an investigation on a career of your choice.**

(a)   What is a career investigation?

2 marks

(b)   (i)   Name a career you investigated.
       (ii)   List the steps that could be used to investigate this career.

5 marks

(c) State **two** Leaving Certificate subjects required for this career.
Explain the relevance of these subjects to your career choice.

6 marks

(d) Describe **two** pathways into your chosen career, using suitable headings.

2015

12 marks

Section C	General Questions	100 marks	Office Use Only	
			1	2

Q.6 Your LCVP class has decided to set up a new Loom Band enterprise to raise funds for a local charity.

(a)   List **four** methods of idea generation.

4 marks

(b)   Questionnaires will be used as part of the market research for this product.
(i)   What is market research?
(ii)   Identify **three** methods, other than questionnaires, used as market research tools.

5 marks

(c) Explain **four** disadvantages of using a questionnaire as a market research tool.

8 marks

(d)   Describe how Information and Communications Technology (ICT) could be used effectively in this enterprise.

8 marks

	Marks Awarded
Section A	
Section B	
Section C	
Q.1	
Q.2	
Q.3	
Q.4	
Q.5	
Q.6	
Total	

	Examination No.

1.	Total of end of page totals.	
2.	Aggregate total of all disallowed answers.	
3.	Total marks awarded (1 minus 2).	

Portfolio Assessment

	Marks Awarded
1	
2	
3	
4	
5	
6	
7	
8	
Total	

1.	Total marks.	
2.	Aggregate total of all disallowed items.	
3.	Total marks awarded (1 minus 2).	

Coimisiún na Scrúduithe Stáit

State Examinations Commission

Leaving Certificate Vocational Programme

Link Modules Examination 2014

Wednesday 7 May 2014, 10.00 – 12.30

INSTRUCTIONS TO CANDIDATES

Examination Number

Write your Examination Number in the box.

Write all answers into this Answer Book.

There are **three** Sections in this Examination.

Section A – Audio Visual

There are **eight** questions.

All questions must be answered.   **(30 marks)**

Section B – Case Study

There are **three** questions.

All questions must be answered.   **(30 marks)**

Section C – General Questions

There are **six** questions.

Four questions must be answered.   **(100 marks)**

2014

Section A	Audio Visual	30 marks

- You will have **three** minutes to read the questions in Section A.
- You will be shown a DVD with a social enterprise theme.
- You will see the DVD **three** times.
  - The first showing will include the whole sequence.
  - It will then be shown in three parts. After each part is shown, you will be given time to write your answers in the appropriate section of the answer book.
  - You will then see the entire DVD sequence again.

This page may be used for notes or to supplement answers.

Section A	Audio Visual	30 marks	Office Use Only	
			1	2
Answer all questions.				
Part 1				
Q.1 What competition has Aoife and her classmates entered?				
		2 marks		
Q.2 Explain why Aoife's class decided to speak to the students who entered the competition last year.				
		2 marks		
Q.3 Describe how Aoife prepared for the presentation.				
		2 marks		

Section A	Audio Visual	30 marks	Office Use Only	
Part 2			1	2
Q.4 Outline how the class intends to successfully complete such a costly project.				
			4 marks	
Q.5 Explain how the class can ensure that their charity shop appeals to teenagers and young people.				

Section A	Audio Visual	30 marks	Office Use Only	
			1	2
		4 marks		

Q.6 Describe **two** planning skills demonstrated by Aoife and her classmates.

	4 marks	

2014

Section A	Audio Visual	30 marks	Office Use Only	
			1	2
Part 3				
Q.7 How did the judges react to Aoife's presentation?				
		6 marks		

Section A	Audio Visual	30 marks	Office Use Only	
			1	2
Q.8 Describe how the project should be evaluated by the class.				
Section A	Audio Visual	30 marks	1	2
Q.8		**6 marks**		

COROBAWN SUMMER FESTIVAL

Corobawn is a small town located in the North West of Ireland with a population of 4,000 people. The town has always attracted hiking and activity enthusiasts due to its location on the Great Western Greenway. Located six kilometres from the town centre is the Corobawn Hotel and Golf Resort. It has managed to prosper in the difficult economic environment by targeting golfers from the UK and US markets. Other than the ruins of an old Abbey, which is currently being restored, there are not many other tourist attractions to lure visitors from the larger towns and the coastline.

The Gathering was designed to encourage local communities to plan special events and highlight what is great about their community and about Ireland. Corobawn had a very successful Gathering weekend in 2013. The weekend Gathering Festival had a variety of events including a 1940's street pageant and dance, a walking festival, guided tours of the town and local area, archive photos and family record displays. The Gathering Festival attracted nearly 5,000 visitors to Corobawn with local bed and breakfasts, the hotel and golf resort, local shops, cafes and restaurants all benefiting from the increase in footfall to the local area.

The town festival committee is meeting to evaluate the success of the previous year's festival and to plan for 2014. As part of the evaluation of last year's festival the committee carried out a visitor survey over the summer months. It was facilitated by local bed and breakfasts and the Corobawn Hotel and Golf Resort. The results of the survey are shown in the graph opposite.

The town festival committee members are determined to build on the success of last year's Gathering Festival and attract new as well as repeat visitors. The committee, representing the local community, is made up of ten enthusiastic members with a variety of skills and experience. They are currently brainstorming ideas for this year's summer festival. Some of the ideas generated include a week-long walking festival with events in the evenings for the hikers, an artisan food festival promoting local food produce and a genealogy presentation called 'Exploring Your Roots in Corobawn'. They would like to develop a web site for the area as well as a social media presence. They also believe that local businesses should be encouraged to take advantage of opportunities to market themselves with Fáilte Ireland.

The festival committee members know from last year's experience that planning is key to ensuring that any community festival is a success. Many committee members believe that Corobawn's location on the Great Western Greenway has not been fully exploited. They also believe that the opening of the Wild Atlantic Way presents significant opportunities for Corobawn. These members believe that there should be a greater emphasis on attracting more hiking and activity enthusiasts to the area. This move has led to some conflict on the committee as other committee members feel that they should simply focus on holding a summer festival.

Section B	Case Study	30 marks	Office Use Only	
			1	2
Answer all questions.				
Q.1 Outline **three** reasons why visitors might come to Corobawn.				
			6 marks	1	2

Section B	Case Study	30 marks	Office Use Only	
Q.2 (i) Explain why the festival committee decided to carry out a survey of visitors to the town in 2013. (ii) Outline how local businesses in Corobawn could promote themselves.			1	2

Section B	Case Study	30 marks	Office Use Only	
			1	2
		12 marks		

Q.3
(i) Explain how the Corobawn festival committee can ensure that meetings are effective.
(ii) Outline the methods the Corobawn festival committee could use to resolve the conflict which has arisen.

12 marks		

INDEX AND SUMMARY

Section C contains six questions of 25 marks each and you should answer **any four**. To assist in deciding and locating the questions to answer, the following is the text of all the questions with the page number range for each. Answer your choice in the appropriate pages that follow in this booklet.

Q.1 **Career Investigation introduces the skills of research and planning**.   **Pages 294 – 296**
- (a) Name the career you investigated as part of your LCVP Link Modules.
- (b) As part of your Career Investigation you interviewed a person working in this career area. Explain how you prepared for this interview.
- (c) State **three** qualities/skills relevant to this career. Explain the reasons why these qualities/skills are relevant to this career.
- (d) Evaluate the different methods of research used in your Career Investigation.

Q.2 **A visit out to a local business is a valuable learning experience for LCVP students**.   **Pages 297 – 299**
- (a) Name the business your LCVP class visited. Outline the type of work carried out by this business.
- (b) Outline the benefits to an LCVP class of visiting a local business.
- (c) Name **three** Leaving Certificate subjects, other than the Link Modules, which you are studying. Explain how **each** subject was useful in the organisation/planning of this visit.
- (d) Describe the steps the business owner/manager can take to ensure the LCVP student visit is a success.

Q.3 **Upskilling, JobBridge and Teamwork are part of modern working life**.   **Pages 300 – 302**
- (a) Explain what is meant by the term 'Upskilling'.
- (b) Outline the reasons why it is important for a worker to engage in upskilling.
- (c) 'JobBridge, the National Internship Scheme, provides work experience opportunities for unemployed people'.
  Explain the benefits for a job seeker of participating in the 'JobBridge' scheme.
- (d) Describe the ways in which an employer can ensure effective teamwork in his/her organisation.

Q.4 **Your LCVP class has decided to run a mini company making plant pot holders**.   **Pages 303 – 305**
- (a) Draft the agenda for the first meeting held to plan this activity.
- (b) An Action Plan will help ensure the success of this activity.
  Outline the benefits of having an Action Plan for this activity.
- (c) Identify the resources needed to run this activity and outline why **each** resource is needed.
- (d) Explain the term 'feedback'. In relation to an enterprise activity explain the type of feedback you could expect to receive.

Q.5 **Voluntary groups/organisations carry out important work in local communities**.   **Pages 306 – 308**
- (a) Name a voluntary group/organisation that operates in your locality. Outline the type of work carried out by this voluntary group/organisation.
- (b) A young person wishes to engage in volunteering. Outline the factors that must be considered when choosing an organisation to volunteer with.
- (c) (i) Voluntary groups/organisations should carry out a SWOT analysis. Explain why a SWOT analysis is beneficial to a voluntary group/organisation.
  - (ii) Complete a SWOT analysis of the voluntary group/organisation referred to in part (a).
- (d) (i) Describe **two** ways a local business can support a voluntary group/organisation in its community.
  - (ii) Analyse the reasons why a business might support a local voluntary group/organisation.

Q.6 **Enterprise**   **Pages 309 – 311**
- (a) State and explain **four** personal characteristics of an entrepreneur.
- (b) Discuss **three** benefits entrepreneurs bring to society.
- (c) Describe **three** possible problems that an entrepreneur may face when starting a business for the first time.
- (d) Explain how the role of an entrepreneur differs from that of a manager in a business.

2014

Section C	General Questions	100 marks	Office Use Only	
			1	2
Q.1 **Career Investigation introduces the skills of research and planning.**				
(a) Name the career you investigated as part of your LCVP Link Modules.				
	1 mark			
(b) As part of your Career Investigation you interviewed a person working in this career area. Explain how you prepared for this interview.				
	6 marks			

(c) State **three** qualities/skills relevant to this career. Explain the reasons why these
     qualities/skills are relevant to this career.

9 marks

2014

(d)   Evaluate the different methods of research used in your Career Investigation.

9 marks

Section C	General Questions	100 marks	Office Use Only	
			1	2
Q.2 **A visit out to a local business is a valuable learning experience for LCVP students.**				
(a) Name the business your LCVP class visited. Outline the type of work carried out by this business.				
		2 marks		
(b) Outline the benefits to an LCVP class of visiting a local business.				
		6 marks		

2014

(c) Name **three** Leaving Certificate subjects, other than the Link Modules, which you are studying. Explain how **each** subject was useful in the organisation/planning of this visit.

9 marks

(d) Describe the steps the business owner/manager can take to ensure the LCVP student visit is a success.

8 marks

Section C	General Questions	100 marks	Office Use Only	
			1	2
Q.3 **Upskilling, JobBridge and Teamwork are part of modern working life.**				
(a) Explain what is meant by the term 'Upskilling'.				
		2 marks		
(b) Outline the reasons why it is important for a worker to engage in upskilling.				
		6 marks	1	2

(c) 'JobBridge, the National Internship Scheme, provides work experience opportunities for unemployed people'.

Explain the benefits for a job seeker of participating in the 'JobBridge' scheme.

8 marks

2014

(d) Describe the ways in which an employer can ensure effective teamwork in his/her organisation.

9 marks

Section C	General Questions	100 marks	Office Use Only	
			1	2

Q.4 Your LCVP class has decided to run a mini company making plant pot holders.

(a)   Draft the agenda for the first meeting held to plan this activity.

6 marks

(b)   An Action Plan will help ensure the success of this activity.
Outline the benefits of having an Action Plan for this activity.

4 marks

2014

(c)   Identify the resources needed to run this activity and outline why **each** resource is needed.

6 marks

(d) Explain the term 'feedback'. In relation to an enterprise activity explain the type of feedback you could expect to receive.

9 marks

Section C	General Questions	100 marks	Office Use Only	
			1	2
Q.5	**Voluntary groups/organisations carry out important work in local communities.**			
(a)	Name a voluntary group/organisation that operates in your locality. Outline the type of work carried out by this voluntary group/organisation.			
		3 marks		
(b)	A young person wishes to engage in volunteering. Outline the factors must be considered when choosing an organisation to volunteer with.			
		4 marks		

(c)	(i)	Voluntary groups/organisations should carry out a SWOT analysis. Explain why a SWOT analysis is beneficial to a voluntary group/organisation.		
	(ii)	Complete a SWOT analysis of the voluntary group/organisation referred to in part (a).		
		10 marks		

2014

(d) (i) Describe **two** ways a local business can support a voluntary group/organisation in its community.

(ii) Analyse the reasons why a business might support a local voluntary group/organisation.

8 marks

Section C	General Questions	100 marks	Office Use Only	
			1	2
Q.6 **Enterprise**				
(a) State and explain **four** personal characteristics of an entrepreneur.				
		4 marks		
(b) Discuss **three** benefits entrepreneurs bring to society.				
		6 marks		

2014

309

(c)   Describe **three** possible problems that an entrepreneur may face when starting a business for the first time.

9 marks

(d) Explain how the role of an entrepreneur differs from that of a manager in a business.

6 marks

SAY NO TO BULLYING
NOBODY DESERVES TO BE BULLIED
TELL AN ADULT YOU CAN TRUST

This Anti-Bullying campaign is supported by the
Department of Education and Skills with the co-operation
of the Irish Educational Publishers Association

Edco 2022/2023 School Year Planner

KEY DATES

● Public Holidays
■ School Holidays
◆ Important Dates

October 2022 mid-term break: All schools will close from Monday 31st October 2022 to Friday 4th November 2022 inclusive.

Christmas 2022: All schools will close on Wednesday 21st December 2022, which will be the final day of the school term. All schools will re-open on Thursday 5th January 2023.

February 2023 mid-term break: Post-Primary schools will close from Monday 13th February 2023 to Friday 17th February 2023 inclusive.

Easter 2023: All schools will close on Friday 31st March 2023, which will be the final day of the school term. All schools will re-open on Monday 17th April 2023.

5th November – CAO application facility opens for 2023 applications

1st February – Normal closing date for CAO applications

1st May – Closing date for late CAO applications

1st July – Change Your Mind CAO Deadline

The start date for the Junior & Leaving Certificate Examinations 2023 will be Wednesday 7th June.

SEPTEMBER
| 1 Thurs | 2 Fri | 3 Sat | 4 Sun | 5 Mon | 6 Tues | 7 Wed | 8 Thurs | 9 Fri | 10 Sat | 11 Sun | 12 Mon | 13 Tues | 14 Wed | 15 Thurs | 16 Fri | 17 Sat | 18 Sun | 19 Mon | 20 Tues | 21 Wed | 22 Thurs | 23 Fri | 24 Sat | 25 Sun | 26 Mon | 27 Tues | 28 Wed | 29 Thurs | 30 Fri |

OCTOBER
| 1 Sat | 2 Sun | 3 Mon | 4 Tues | 5 Wed | 6 Thurs | 7 Fri | 8 Sat | 9 Sun | 10 Mon | 11 Tues | 12 Wed | 13 Thurs | 14 Fri | 15 Sat | 16 Sun | 17 Mon | 18 Tues | 19 Wed | 20 Thurs | 21 Fri | 22 Sat | 23 Sun | 24 Mon | 25 Tues | 26 Wed | 27 Thurs | 28 Fri | 29 Sat | 30 Sun | 31 Mon |

NOVEMBER
| 1 Tues | 2 Wed | 3 Thurs | 4 Fri | 5 Sat | 6 Sun | 7 Mon | 8 Tues | 9 Wed | 10 Thurs | 11 Fri | 12 Sat | 13 Sun | 14 Mon | 15 Tues | 16 Wed | 17 Thurs | 18 Fri | 19 Sat | 20 Sun | 21 Mon | 22 Tues | 23 Wed | 24 Thurs | 25 Fri | 26 Sat | 27 Sun | 28 Mon | 29 Tues | 30 Wed |

DECEMBER
| 1 Thurs | 2 Fri | 3 Sat | 4 Sun | 5 Mon | 6 Tues | 7 Wed | 8 Thurs | 9 Fri | 10 Sat | 11 Sun | 12 Mon | 13 Tues | 14 Wed | 15 Thurs | 16 Fri | 17 Sat | 18 Sun | 19 Mon | 20 Tues | 21 Wed | 22 Thurs | 23 Fri | 24 Sat | 25 Sun | 26 Mon | 27 Tues | 28 Wed | 29 Thurs | 30 Fri | 31 Sat |

JANUARY
| 1 Sun | 2 Mon | 3 Tues | 4 Wed | 5 Thurs | 6 Fri | 7 Sat | 8 Sun | 9 Mon | 10 Tues | 11 Wed | 12 Thurs | 13 Fri | 14 Sat | 15 Sun | 16 Mon | 17 Tues | 18 Wed | 19 Thurs | 20 Fri | 21 Sat | 22 Sun | 23 Mon | 24 Tues | 25 Wed | 26 Thurs | 27 Fri | 28 Sat | 29 Sun | 30 Mon | 31 Tues |

FEBRUARY
| 1 Wed | 2 Thurs | 3 Fri | 4 Sat | 5 Sun | 6 Mon | 7 Tues | 8 Wed | 9 Thurs | 10 Fri | 11 Sat | 12 Sun | 13 Mon | 14 Tues | 15 Wed | 16 Thurs | 17 Fri | 18 Sat | 19 Sun | 20 Mon | 21 Tues | 22 Wed | 23 Thurs | 24 Fri | 25 Sat | 26 Sun | 27 Mon | 28 Tues |

MARCH
| 1 Wed | 2 Thurs | 3 Fri | 4 Sat | 5 Sun | 6 Mon | 7 Tues | 8 Wed | 9 Thurs | 10 Fri | 11 Sat | 12 Sun | 13 Mon | 14 Tues | 15 Wed | 16 Thurs | 17 Fri | 18 Sat | 19 Sun | 20 Mon | 21 Tues | 22 Wed | 23 Thurs | 24 Fri | 25 Sat | 26 Sun | 27 Mon | 28 Tues | 29 Wed | 30 Thurs | 31 Fri |

APRIL
| 1 Sat | 2 Sun | 3 Mon | 4 Tues | 5 Wed | 6 Thurs | 7 Fri | 8 Sat | 9 Sun | 10 Mon | 11 Tues | 12 Wed | 13 Thurs | 14 Fri | 15 Sat | 16 Sun | 17 Mon | 18 Tues | 19 Wed | 20 Thurs | 21 Fri | 22 Sat | 23 Sun | 24 Mon | 25 Tues | 26 Wed | 27 Thurs | 28 Fri | 29 Sat | 30 Sun |

MAY
| 1 Mon | 2 Tues | 3 Wed | 4 Thurs | 5 Fri | 6 Sat | 7 Sun | 8 Mon | 9 Tues | 10 Wed | 11 Thurs | 12 Fri | 13 Sat | 14 Sun | 15 Mon | 16 Tues | 17 Wed | 18 Thurs | 19 Fri | 20 Sat | 21 Sun | 22 Mon | 23 Tues | 24 Wed | 25 Thurs | 26 Fri | 27 Sat | 28 Sun | 29 Mon | 30 Tues | 31 Wed |

JUNE
| 1 Thurs | 2 Fri | 3 Sat | 4 Sun | 5 Mon | 6 Tues | 7 Wed | 8 Thurs | 9 Fri | 10 Sat | 11 Sun | 12 Mon | 13 Tues | 14 Wed | 15 Thurs | 16 Fri | 17 Sat | 18 Sun | 19 Mon | 20 Tues | 21 Wed | 22 Thurs | 23 Fri | 24 Sat | 25 Sun | 26 Mon | 27 Tues | 28 Wed | 29 Thurs | 30 Fri |

JULY
| 1 Sat | 2 Sun | 3 Mon | 4 Tues | 5 Wed | 6 Thurs | 7 Fri | 8 Sat | 9 Sun | 10 Mon | 11 Tues | 12 Wed | 13 Thurs | 14 Fri | 15 Sat | 16 Sun | 17 Mon | 18 Tues | 19 Wed | 20 Thurs | 21 Fri | 22 Sat | 23 Sun | 24 Mon | 25 Tues | 26 Wed | 27 Thurs | 28 Fri | 29 Sat | 30 Sun | 31 Mon |

AUGUST
| 1 Tues | 2 Wed | 3 Thurs | 4 Fri | 5 Sat | 6 Sun | 7 Mon | 8 Tues | 9 Wed | 10 Thurs | 11 Fri | 12 Sat | 13 Sun | 14 Mon | 15 Tues | 16 Wed | 17 Thurs | 18 Fri | 19 Sat | 20 Sun | 21 Mon | 22 Tues | 23 Wed | 24 Thurs | 25 Fri | 26 Sat | 27 Sun | 28 Mon | 29 Tues | 30 Wed | 31 Thurs |